Gold Stars®

Big Workbook

Maths, English & Science

AGES 7-9

KEY STAGE 2

PaRragon

Bath · New York · Cologne · Melbourne · Delhi
Hong Kong · Shenzhen · Singapore

Written by Nina Filipek, Paul Broadbent and Peter Riley
Illustrated by Rob Davis/www.the-art-agency.co.uk
and Tom Connell/www.the-art-agency.co.uk
Educational consultants: Ann Dicks, Martin Malcolm and Catherine Casey

This edition published by Parragon Books Ltd in 2018

Parragon Books Ltd
Chartist House
15–17 Trim Street
Bath BA1 1HA, UK
www.parragon.com

ISBN 978-1-5270-0232-6

Printed in China

Parents' notes

The Gold Stars Key Stage 2 series

The Gold Stars Key Stage 2 series has been created to help your child practise key skills and information learned in school. Each book has been written by an expert team of teachers. The books will help your child to consolidate key skills in Maths, English and Science, helping to develop confidence and understanding of these topics.

How to use the Key Stage 2 series

- Talk through the introductions to each topic and review the examples together.

- Encourage your child to tackle the fill-in activities independently.

- Keep work times short. Skip a page if it seems too difficult and return to it later.

- It doesn't matter if your child does some of the pages out of order.

- Your child does not need to answer the questions in complete sentences.

- Check the answers on pages 174-184. Encourage effort and reward achievement with praise.

- If your child finds any of the pages too difficult, don't worry. Children learn at different rates.

Contents

Maths

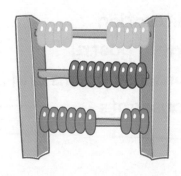

Contents

English

Contents

Science

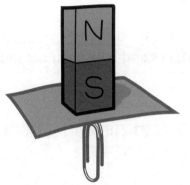

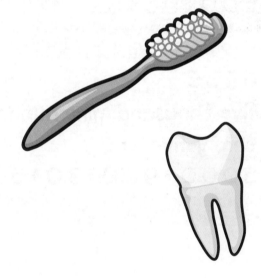

Place value

Learning objective: to learn how 3-digit and 4-digit numbers are made

3-digit numbers are made from hundreds, tens and units. 4-digit numbers are made from thousands, hundreds, tens and units.

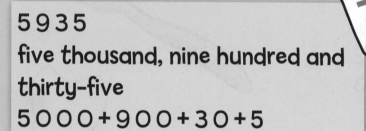

Look at these numbers and how they are made:

593
five hundred and ninety-three
593 =
500 + 90 + 3

5935
five thousand, nine hundred and thirty-five
5000 + 900 + 30 + 5

The position of a digit in a number is really important. 593 and 5935 use the same digits but are different numbers. The position of the digits 0 to 9 gives the value of the number.

A

Write how many thousands, hundreds, tens and units there are in each of these 3-digit or 4-digit numbers.

1. 398 = __3__ + __90__ + __8__

2. 217 = __2__ + __10__ + __7__

3. 3709 = __3__ + __70__ + __90__ + __9__

DEFINITION

digit: Numbers are made up of the digits 0, 1, 2, 3, 4, 5, 6, 7, 8 and 9.

B Write the missing numbers or words to complete each of these.

1. 9 4 1 → nine hundred and _____

2. _____ → three hundred and twenty-six

3. 5 3 4 → _____

4. 2 8 7 0 → _____

5. _____ → one thousand, two hundred and nineteen

6. _____ → two thousand, six hundred and fifty

C Write the numbers shown on each abacus. The first one is done for you.

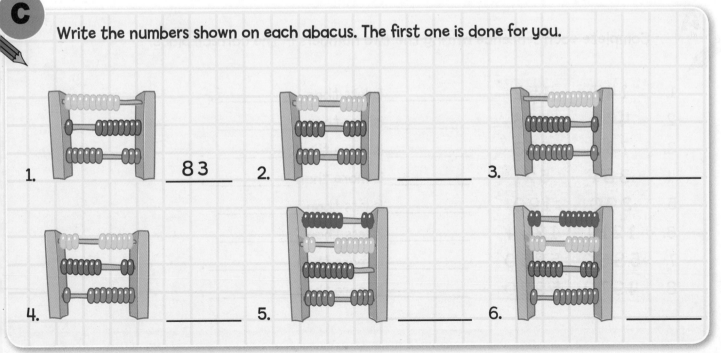

1. __83__ 2. _____ 3. _____

4. _____ 5. _____ 6. _____

Ordering numbers

Learning objective: to compare 3-digit and 4-digit numbers and put them in order

> is the sign for 'is more than'.
< is the sign for 'is less than'.
= is the sign for 'is equal to'.

198 > 168
198 is more than 168.

1126 < 2111
1126 is less than 2111.

Look at the shape of the sign. The number next to the arrow point is smaller than the number on the other side.

You have to compare each digit in the numbers to order them.

A

Complete each sentence writing the two numbers in the correct place.

1.	147	152	_____ is less than _____ .
2.	479	476	_____ is less than _____ .
3.	735	753	_____ is more than _____ .
4.	381	521	_____ is more than _____ .
5.	390	190	_____ is less than _____ .
6.	1214	1244	_____ is less than _____ .
7.	5860	5850	_____ is more than _____ .
8.	4970	5920	_____ is more than _____ .

DEFINITION

ordering numbers: Placing numbers in order from the greatest to the smallest, or the smallest to the greatest.

B Write in the missing < or > signs for each pair of numbers.

1. 264 _____ 254

2. 328 _____ 431

3. 190 _____ 119

4. 1536 _____ 1523

5. 2708 _____ 2807

6. 6550 _____ 6350

C Write each group of numbers in order starting with the smallest.

1. 159   191   112   125   ____ ____ ____ ____

2. 373   387   278   483   ____ ____ ____ ____

3. 645   668   622   739   ____ ____ ____ ____

4. 1461 2416 2460 1410 ____ ____ ____ ____

5. 2743 3778 2760 3704 ____ ____ ____ ____

6. 4815 3309 3459 4195 ____ ____ ____ ____

Number sequences

Learning objective: to continue number sequences by counting on or back in steps

A number sequence is a list of numbers in a pattern. To find the rule or pattern in a sequence try finding the difference between each number.

$$25 \xrightarrow{+25} 50 \xrightarrow{+25} 75 \xrightarrow{+25} 100 \xrightarrow{+25} 125$$

The rule or pattern is +25.

$$150 \xrightarrow{-50} 100 \xrightarrow{-50} 50 \xrightarrow{-50} 0 \xrightarrow{-50} -50$$

The rule or pattern is -50.
This number sequence goes down below zero. Numbers below zero are called negative numbers and are written with a minus sign in front of them.

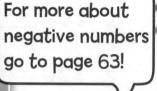

For more about negative numbers go to page 63!

A Write the next two numbers in each sequence.

1. 110   100   90   80   ____ ____

2. 100   75   50   25   ____ ____

3. 225   200   175   150   ____ ____

4. 720   620   520   420   ____ ____

5. 350   375   400   425   ____ ____

6. 550   500   450   400   ____ ____

7. 1968 1868 1768 1668 ____ ____

8. 1931 2931 3931 4931 ____ ____

If you find these activities easy peasy, stretch your brain with the next tricky challenges!

14

B Write the missing numbers and the rule or pattern for each number sequence.

1.	70	___	100	115	130	___	The rule is : ___
2.	650	600	550	___	___	400	The rule is : ___
3.	___	843	___	643	543	443	The rule is : ___
4.	719	___	519	___	319	219	The rule is : ___
5.	___	825	830	835	___	845	The rule is : ___
6.	462	___	482	492	___	512	The rule is : ___
7.	133	123	___	___	93	83	The rule is : ___
8.	___	515	518	521	524	___	The rule is : ___

C Two numbers in each sequence have been swapped over. Circle the two numbers out of place in each sequence. Write each correct sequence.

1. 975   985   995   965   955   945   935

___   ___   ___   ___   ___   ___

2. 80   180   280   380   680   580   480

___   ___   ___   ___   ___   ___

3. 853   855   857   851   849   847   845

___   ___   ___   ___   ___   ___

Number trios

Learning objective: to know addition and subtraction facts

If you know an addition fact, you can work out
a related subtraction fact.

Learning
number trios is
really useful.

Use trios of numbers, such as 11, 4 and 7, to learn the facts.

(11) (4) (7)

$4 + 7 = 11$ $\qquad$ $11 - 4 = 7$

$7 + 4 = 11$ $\qquad$ $11 - 7 = 4$

Use addition and subtraction facts to help with larger numbers.

$6 + 3 = 9$ $\qquad$ $9 - 3 = 6$

$60 + 30 = 90$ $\qquad$ $90 - 30 = 60$

$600 + 300 = 900$ $\qquad$ $900 - 300 = 600$

A Write the addition and subtraction families for each trio.

1.

| 7 | 8 | 15 |

___ + ___ = ___ $\qquad$ ___ − ___ = ___

___ + ___ = ___ $\qquad$ ___ − ___ = ___

2.

| 6 | 12 | 6 |

___ + ___ = ___ $\qquad$ ___ − ___ = ___

___ + ___ = ___ $\qquad$ ___ − ___ = ___

3.

| 9 | 14 | 5 |

___ + ___ = ___ $\qquad$ ___ − ___ = ___

___ + ___ = ___ $\qquad$ ___ − ___ = ___

4.

| 9 | 7 | 16 |

___ + ___ = ___ $\qquad$ ___ − ___ = ___

___ + ___ = ___ $\qquad$ ___ − ___ = ___

B

Answer these.

1. 6 + 9 = _____

    60 + 90 = _____

    600 + 900 = _____

2. 8 - 4 = _____

    80 - 40 = _____

    800 - 400 = _____

3. 7 + 5 = _____

    70 + 50 = _____

    700 + 500 = _____

4. 9 - 7 = _____

    90 - 70 = _____

    900 - 700 = _____

C

Write the missing numbers.

1. 6 + ☐ = 15

2. 13 − ☐ = 5

3. ☐ − 9 = 9

4. ☐ + 8 = 12

5. 40 + ☐ = 100

6. ☐ − 200 = 700

7. 80 − ☐ = 30

8. ☐ + 400 = 600

D

Work these out in your head.

1. What is the sum of 50 and 40? _____

2. What is the total of 6 and 8? _____

4. Which number is 300 less than 900? _____

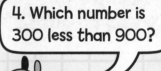

5. What is 200 more than 500? _____

3. What is the difference between 14 and 7? _____

6. What is 80 subtract 40? _____

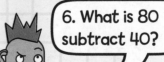

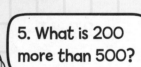

17

Mental addition

Learning objective: to mentally add 1-, 2- and 3-digit numbers

Break numbers up so that you can add them in your head.

What is 34 add 25?

34 + 25 =
30 + 20 + 4 + 5 =
50 + 4 + 5 =
50 + 9 = 59

Add the tens then add the units.

Add together 123 and 40.

123 + 40 =
100 + 20 + 40 + 3 =
100 + 60 + 3 =
100 + 60 + 3 = 163

Add the hundreds, then the tens, then the units.

A

Add these in your head and write the answers.

1. $63 + 4 =$

2. $51 + 6 =$

3. $32 + 3 =$

4. $22 + 7 =$

5. $194 + 4 =$

6. $173 + 5 =$

B

Add these in your head and write the answers.

1. $56 + 20 =$

2. $38 + 40 =$

3. $52 + 30 =$

4. $23 + 20 =$

5. $110 + 70 =$

6. $130 + 60 =$

C Join the pairs of sums with the same total.

$55+20=$ ☐

$129+50=$ ☐

$62+6 =$ ☐

$72+3=$ ☐

$171+8=$ ☐

$48+20=$ ☐

$137+30=$ ☐

$49+40 =$ ☐

$84+5 =$ ☐

$163+4=$ ☐

D Read the first statement then work out the answers to the questions in your head.

My mother is 34.

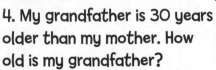

1. My aunt is 3 years older than my mother. How old is my aunt?

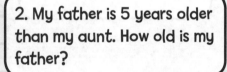

2. My father is 5 years older than my aunt. How old is my father?

3. My grandmother was 20 when my mother was born. How old is my grandmother?

_____

_____

_____

4. My grandfather is 30 years older than my mother. How old is my grandfather?

5. My uncle is 4 years older than my father. How old is my uncle?

6. My great-grandmother is 50 years older than my mother. How old is my great-grandmother?

_____

_____

_____

19

Mental subtraction

Learning objective: to mentally subtract 1-, 2-, and 3-digit numbers

Break up numbers so that you can subtract them in your head.

What is 37 subtract 5?

37 – 5 =

30 + 7 – 5 =
30 + 7 – 5 = 32

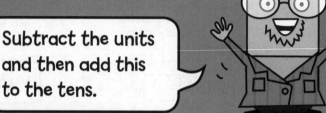

Subtract the units
and then add this
to the tens.

Take away 130 from 154.
154 – 130 =

54 – 30 = 24
100 – 100 = 0
54 – 30 + 100 – 100 = 24

Subtract the tens
and units, then
the hundreds.

A

Break up these numbers to subtract them in your head.

1. 46 – 4 =_____

2. 87 – 3 =_____

3. 29 – 6 =_____

4. 178 – 50 =_____

5. 93 – 30 =_____

6. 52 – 40 =_____

7. 72 – 30 =_____

8. 165 – 3 =_____

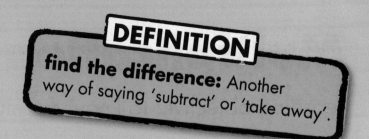

DEFINITION

find the difference: Another way of saying 'subtract' or 'take away'.

B

Find the difference between each pair of numbers.

1. | 98 | | 3 | _____

2. | 5 | | 57 | _____

3. | 3 | | 76 | _____

4. | 282 | | 40 | _____

5. | 120 | | 44 | _____

6. | 150 | | 91 | _____

C

Complete each chart to show the numbers coming out of each subtraction machine.

1. IN 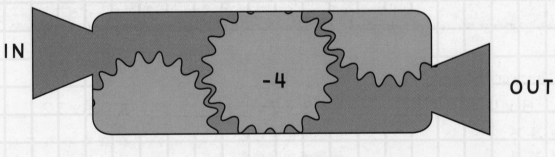 OUT

-4

IN	56	78	27	49	15	64
OUT	52					

2. IN OUT

-30

IN	165	191	142	177	159	183
OUT	135					

Multiplication facts

Learning objective: to know the multiplication facts up to 12 x 12

Use the multiplication facts you already know to help learn other facts.

Example

3 x 5 = 15	8 x 2 = 16	10 x 6 = 60
3 x 6 is 3 more → 18	8 x 4 is double 16 → 32	9 x 6 is 6 less → 54

Remember 7 x 3 gives the same answer as 3 x 7.

It's easy when you know the facts!

A Answer these.

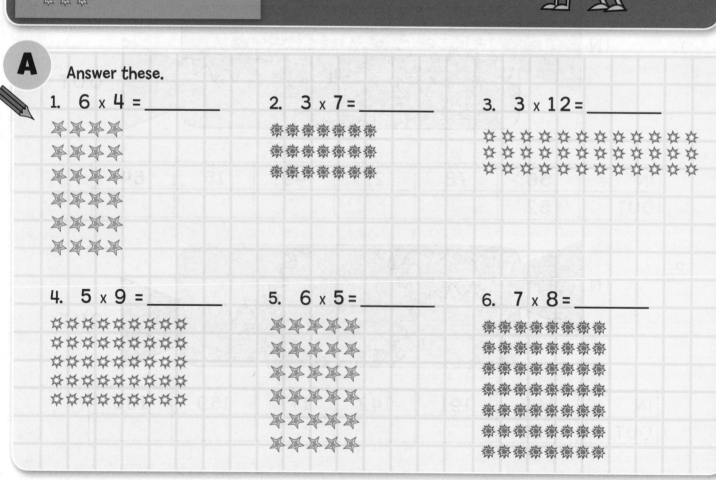

1. 6 x 4 = _____

2. 3 x 7 = _____

3. 3 x 12 = _____

4. 5 x 9 = _____

5. 6 x 5 = _____

6. 7 x 8 = _____

DEFINITION

multiplication fact: It is true that 3 x 5 = 15. This is a multiplication fact.

B

Write the answers for each of these.

1. 5 x 7 = _____
   6 x 7 = _____

2. 5 x 8 = _____
   6 x 8 = _____

3. 10 x 6 = _____
   9 x 6 = _____

4. 12 x 8 = _____
   11 x 8 = _____

5. 3 x 3 = _____
   6 x 3 = _____

6. 2 x 12 = _____
   4 x 12 = _____

7. 4 x 4 = _____
   8 x 4 = _____

8. 2 x 9 = _____
   4 x 9 = _____

C

Look at the pictures and answer the questions.

1. Julie buys 4 packs of plates. What is the total number of plates she has? _____

2. Sam buys 3 packs of straws. How many straws does he have in total? _____

3. Owen wants 12 glasses. How many packs of glasses will he need to buy? _____

4. Owen also wants 12 plates. How many packs of plates will he need to buy? _____

5. Sabina wants 20 glasses. How many packs of glasses will she need to buy? _____

6. Tess wants 20 straws. How many packs of straws does she need to buy? _____

Now see if you can complete this challenge!

D

| 2 | x | ☐ | → 18 | | ☐ | x | 7 | → 28 |

x   x   x   x

| ☐ | x | ☐ | → 54 | | ☐ | x | ☐ | → 27 |

↓   ↓   ↓   ↓

12   81   36   21

23

Written addition

Learning objective: to add 2-, 3- and 4-digit numbers

When you can't work out an addition in your head, try a written method.

Example 1

138 + 54

$$100 + 30 + 8$$
$$+ \quad\quad\; 50 + 4$$
$$\overline{100 + 80 + 12} \rightarrow 100 + 80 + 12 = 192$$

With this short method, add the units, tens and then the hundreds.

$$138$$
$$+ \;\; 54$$
$$\overline{192}$$
$$\;\;\; 1$$

Example 2

1241 + 329

$$1000 + 200 + 40 + 1$$
$$+ \quad\quad\;\; 300 + 20 + 9$$
$$\overline{1000 + 500 + 60 + 10}$$

$$\rightarrow 1000 + 500 + 60 + 10 = 1570$$

With this short method, add the units, tens, hundreds and then thousands.

$$1241$$
$$+ \;\; 329$$
$$\overline{1570}$$
$$\quad\;\; 1$$

Make sure you line up the digits correctly.

A Add these and write the answers.

1. $267 + 18 \rightarrow$

	200	+	60	+ 7
+			10	+ 8
	+		+	= ___

2. $109 + 79 \rightarrow$

	100	+	0	+ 9
+			70	+ 9
	+		+	= ___

B

Now write the answers to these.

1. 143
   + 37
   _____

2. 215
   +129
   _____

3. 2238
   + 58
   _____

4. 2126
   + 135
   _____

C

Read and answer these. Use paper for your working out.

1. What is 15 more than 78? _____

2. Add 57 and 26. _____

3. What is the total of 33 and 39? _____

4. Increase 124 by 47. _____

5. Total 265 and 29. _____

6. What is 246 added to 1205? _____

D

Read and answer these problems. Use paper for your working out.

1. A truck driver travels 53 kilometres in the morning and 37 kilometres in the afternoon.
   How far does the truck travel in total? _____

2. A market stall sells 28 bottles of mango juice and 39 bottles of orange juice.
   What is the total number of bottles sold? _____

3. A farmer has 44 chickens and 17 ducks.
   How many chickens and ducks are there altogether? _____

4. A postman has 149 letters and 36 parcels.
   How many items altogether are there to deliver? _____

5. Jamal has read 108 pages of his reading book and there are 52 pages left.
   How many pages in total are there in Jamal's reading book? _____

6. Julie is 136 centimetres tall and her dad is 38 centimetres taller than she is.
   How tall is Julie's dad? _____

Written subtraction

Learning objective: to subtract 2-, 3- and 4-digit numbers

When you can't work out a subtraction in your head, try a written method.

Example 1

$$245 = 200 + 40 + 5$$
$$- 64 = \quad\quad 60 + 4$$

$$= 100 + 140 + 5$$
$$- \quad\quad 60 + 4$$
$$= 100 + 80 + 1$$

$$= 181$$

$${}^1\!2\,{}^{14}\!4\,5$$
$$-\quad 6\,4$$
$$\quad 1\,8\,1$$

Subtract the units first, then the tens, then the hundreds. However, in this example, in the tens column we cannot subtract 6 from 4 because that would take us below zero. When this happens we need to 'borrow' from the next column along.

Example 2

$$4567 = 4000 + 500 + 60 + 7$$
$$- 893 = \quad\quad\quad 800 + 90 + 3$$

$$= 4000 + 400 + 160 + 7$$
$$- \quad\quad\quad 800 + 90 + 3$$

$$= 3000 + 1400 + 160 + 7$$
$$- \quad\quad\quad\quad 800 + 90 + 3$$
$$= 3000 + 600 + 70 + 4$$

$$\longrightarrow \quad 4\,{}^4\!5\,{}^{16}\!6\,7$$
$$-\quad 8\,9\,3$$

$$\longrightarrow \quad {}^3\!4\,{}^{14}\!5\,{}^{16}\!6\,7$$
$$-\quad 8\,9\,3$$
$$\quad 3\,6\,7\,4$$

Now let's try with some thousands, too!

A Answer these. Use a separate piece of paper for your workings out if you need to.

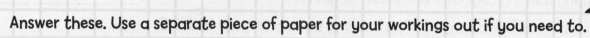
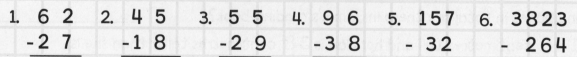

1. 6 2   2. 4 5   3. 5 5   4. 9 6   5. 1 5 7   6. 3 8 2 3
   -2 7   -1 8   -2 9   -3 8   - 3 2   - 2 6 4

Don't forget to start with the units!

B

Read and answer these. Use a separate piece of paper for your workings out if you need to.

1. What is the difference between 28 and 48? _____

2. Subtract 16 from 43. _____

3. What number is 34 less than 456? _____

4. What is 880 take away 729? _____

5. How much greater is 2391 than 776? _____

6. What is 7866 minus 4937? _____

C

Now try this cool number puzzle!

a) 2		b)	c)	
2	d)			e)
f)		g)	h)	
	i)			j)

The puzzle works like a crossword. Solve the clues and write one digit in each space. Question (a) down has been done for you.

Clues

Across	Down
a) 53 – 26	a) 44 – 22
c) 60 – 21	b) 31 – 16
d) 455 – 96	d) 42 – 11
f) 65 – 24	e) 60 – 15
h) 41 – 26	f) 72 – 26
i) 541 – 63	g) 64 – 27
j) 57 – 49	

Multiplication

Learning objective: to multiply 2- and 3-digit numbers by a 1-digit number

There are different methods for multiplying numbers.

Example 1

What is 38 multiplied by 5?

38 x 5 ⟶ 30 x 5 = 150
             8 x 5 = 40 +
            38 x 5 = 190

Example 2

What is 124 multiplied by 6?

x	100	20	4
6	600	120	24

⟶ 600 + 120 + 24 = 744

A Complete these multiplications.

1. 14 x 4 ⟶   10 x 4 =
                 4 x 4 = _____ +
                14 x 4 =

2. 25 x 9 ⟶ 20 x 9 =
                5 x 9 = _____ +
               25 x 9 =

3. 37 x 6 ⟶   30 x 6 =
                 7 x 6 = _____ +
                37 x 6 =

4. 58 x 3 ⟶ 50 x 3 =
                8 x 3 = _____ +
               58 x 3 =

B Complete these multiplications using a grid.

1. 76 x 2 = _____

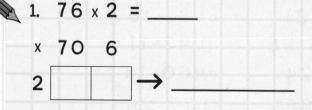

x	70	6
2		

⟶ _____

2. 23 x 8 = _____

x	20	3
8		

⟶ _____

3. 137 x 5 = _____

x	100	30	7
5			

⟶ _____

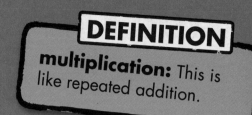

C

Answer these. Choose a method for working out each answer. Use paper for your working out.

1. 8 6 x 2 = _____

2. 4 7 x 3 = _____

3. 1 9 x 9 = _____

4. 2 3 x 8 = _____

5. 1 3 4 x 6 = _____

6. 1 2 8 x 5 = _____

D

Read and answer these problems.

1. A bus holds 48 passengers. How many people will 4 buses hold?

   _____

2. Mr Duke travels 19 kilometres each day to and from work. He works 5 days a week. How far does he travel altogether in a week?

   _____

3. A market stall has 6 crates of melons. There are 35 melons in a crate. How many melons are there in total?

   _____

4. A farmer fills 4 trays of eggs. Each tray holds 36 eggs. How many eggs does the farmer have?

   _____

5. The battery in a mobile phone lasts 7 days. How many hours does the battery last?

   _____

6. A dog eats 59 dog biscuits per day. How many will it eat in 3 days?

   _____

Break the problem down into smaller steps.

Use the multiplication facts that you know.

29

Division

Learning objective: to use written methods to divide

If you know your multiplication facts it can help you to divide numbers.

Look at the trio 6, 3 and 18:

$6 \times 3 = 18$ $3 \times 6 = 18$

$18 \div 3 = 6$ $18 \div 6 = 3$

If a number cannot be divided exactly it leaves a remainder.

Example

What is 35 divided by 4?

Work out how many groups of 4 are in 35 and what is left over:

```
        8 r 3  ←──────────  Answer
    4 ) 3 5
      - 3 2   (4 x 8)
        3              35 ÷ 4 = 8 remainder 3
```

Division is the opposite of multiplication.

A

Copy and complete these and find the remainders.

1.
```
          r ___
  5 / 4 8
  - ___ (5 x 9)
  ___
```

2.
```
          r ___
  6 / 3 7
  - ___ (6 x 6)
  ___
```

3.
```
          r ___
  9 / 6 5
  - ___ (9 x 7)
  ___
```

4.
```
          r ___
  3 / 2 6
  - ___ (__ x __)
  ___
```

5.
```
          r ___
  7 / 4 0
  - ___ (__ x __)
  ___
```

6.
```
          r ___
  8 / 5 2
  - ___ (__ x __)
  ___
```

B

Complete these.

1. ___ ÷ 4 = 7

2. 18 ÷ ___ = 2

3. ___ x 6 = 36

4. 40 ÷ 5 = ___

5. 8 x ___ = 24

6. ___ x 7 = 21

7. 54 ÷ ___ = 9

8. 6 x ___ = 48

9. 63 ÷ 9 = ___

10. ___ ÷ 4 = 8

I'm thinking of a number. It is less than 100 and if I divide it by 2, 3, 4, 5, 6 or 10 it leaves a remainder of 1. What is my number?

C

Mrs Folkes is grouping her class into teams. She has 35 pupils in her class.

Read and answer these questions.

1. The School Maths Quiz has 3 pupils in each team. How many quiz teams can be made from Mrs Folkes's class? _____

2. Each class is divided into Eco Teams with 8 pupils in each team. Any pupils left over will join children from another class. How many pupils will be left over from Mrs Folkes's class after the Eco Teams are formed? _____

3. Mrs Folkes is dividing her class into sports teams. Complete this chart.

Sport	Number of players in each team	Total number of teams	Number of pupils left over
Doubles Tennis	2 players per team	17 teams	1 left over
400m Relay Race	4 players per team	8 teams	
Basketball	5 players per team		0 left over
Volleyball	6 players per team		
Netball	7 players per team		

31

Fractions of quantities

Learning objective: to find fractions of numbers and quantities

Fractions have a numerator and a denominator.

$$\frac{3}{4} \leftarrow \text{numerator}$$

denominator $\longrightarrow$ 4

Example 1

What is $\frac{1}{5}$ of 40?

When the numerator is 1, just divide by the denominator.

$\frac{1}{5}$ of 40 = 40 ÷ 5 = 8

Example 2

What is $\frac{3}{5}$ of 40?

When the numerator is more than 1, divide by the denominator then multiply by the numerator.

$\frac{1}{5}$ of 40 = 8

$\frac{3}{5} = \frac{1}{5} \times 3$ $(\frac{1}{5} + \frac{1}{5} + \frac{1}{5})$

so, $\frac{3}{5}$ of 40 = 8 × 3 = 24

A

Use the dots to work out these fractions.

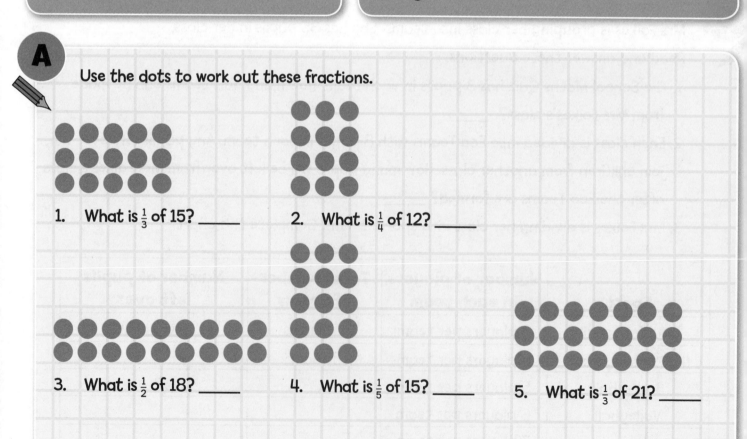

1. What is $\frac{1}{3}$ of 15? _____

2. What is $\frac{1}{4}$ of 12? _____

3. What is $\frac{1}{2}$ of 18? _____

4. What is $\frac{1}{5}$ of 15? _____

5. What is $\frac{1}{3}$ of 21? _____

DEFINITION

fraction: This is a part of a whole.
quantity: How much of something there is.

B

There are 24 balloons of different shapes and colours in a pack. How many of each type of balloon are there?

$\frac{1}{2}$ are red: _____ red balloons

$\frac{1}{6}$ are yellow: _____ yellow balloons

$\frac{1}{3}$ are blue: _____ blue balloons

$\frac{1}{4}$ are large balloons: _____ large balloons

$\frac{1}{8}$ are long balloons: _____ long balloons

24 ASSORTED BALLOONS

David has 64 sweets. He gives $\frac{3}{4}$ to his classmates. How many does he have left?

C

Answer each pair of questions.

1. $\frac{1}{5}$ of 35 = _____

   $\frac{2}{5}$ of 35 = _____

2. $\frac{1}{4}$ of 40 = _____

   $\frac{3}{4}$ of 40 = _____

3. $\frac{1}{7}$ of 21 = _____

   $\frac{5}{7}$ of 21 = _____

4. $\frac{1}{9}$ of 18 = _____

   $\frac{8}{9}$ of 18 = _____

5. $\frac{1}{10}$ of 70 = _____

   $\frac{7}{10}$ of 70 = _____

6. $\frac{1}{8}$ of 32 = _____

   $\frac{7}{8}$ of 32 = _____

7. $\frac{1}{3}$ of 33 = _____

   $\frac{2}{3}$ of 33 = _____

8. $\frac{1}{6}$ of 30 = _____

   $\frac{5}{6}$ of 30 = _____

Use multiplication and division facts to solve these.

33

Decimals

Learning objective: to use and understand tenths

A decimal point is used to separate whole numbers from tenths.
The digit after the decimal point shows the number of tenths.

Tenths break up a whole number into 10 equal parts.

$$\frac{1}{10} = 0.1 \qquad \frac{2}{10} = 0.2 \qquad \frac{3}{10} = 0.3$$

Example
15.7

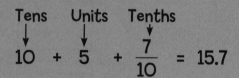

Tens   Units   Tenths

$$10 + 5 + \frac{7}{10} = 15.7$$

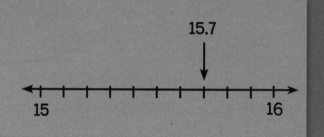

A

Write these fractions as decimals.

1. $6\frac{3}{10}$ _____

2. $\frac{9}{10}$ _____

3. $12\frac{4}{10}$ _____

4. $18\frac{5}{10}$ _____

5. $11\frac{1}{10}$ _____

Write these decimals as fractions.

6. 0.8 _____

7. 7.2 _____

8. 16.7 _____

9. 20.6 _____

10. 4.9 _____

B

Write the value of the digit 2 in each number. Choose from 20, 2 or $\frac{2}{10}$.

1. 12.4 _____

2. 25.5 _____

3. 16.2 _____

4. 3.2 _____

5. 0.2 _____

6. 42.1 _____

34

C

Look at these number lines and write the decimal number above each arrow.

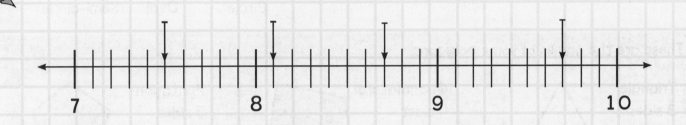

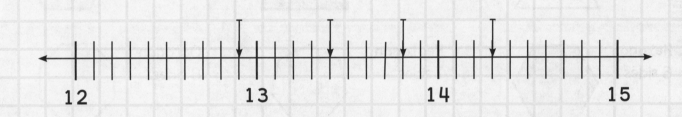

D

Write < or > between these numbers. Use the number lines above to help.

1. 7.6 _____ 7.3

2. 8.9 _____ 9.8

3. 13.4 _____ 12.4

4. 7.5 _____ 9.1

5. $9\frac{2}{10}$ _____ $7\frac{2}{10}$

6. $13\frac{9}{10}$ _____ $13\frac{8}{10}$

7. $8\frac{1}{10}$ _____ $9\frac{3}{10}$

8. $12\frac{4}{10}$ _____ $14\frac{2}{10}$

Look back at page 12 to find out what < and > mean.

2-D shapes

2-D shapes are flat shapes. They can have straight or curved sides.

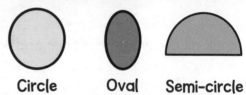

Circle   Oval   Semi-circle

These are the names of some polygons.

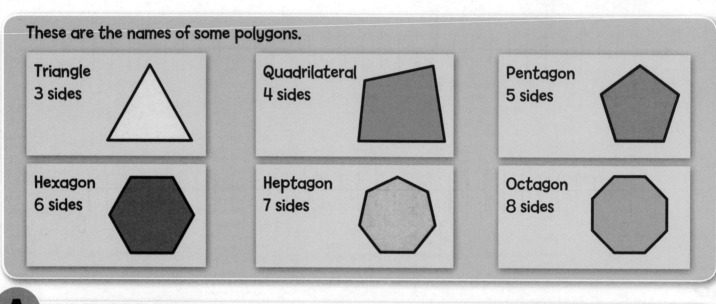

Triangle
3 sides

Quadrilateral
4 sides

Pentagon
5 sides

Hexagon
6 sides

Heptagon
7 sides

Octagon
8 sides

A   Write the name for each shape. Count the number of sides to help find the shape name.

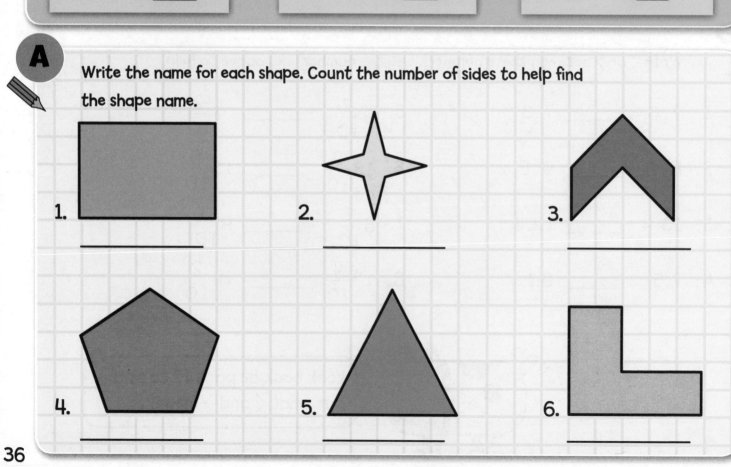

1. _____

2. _____

3. _____

4. _____

5. _____

6. _____

36

B Write the name of the shapes in each set and the odd one out.

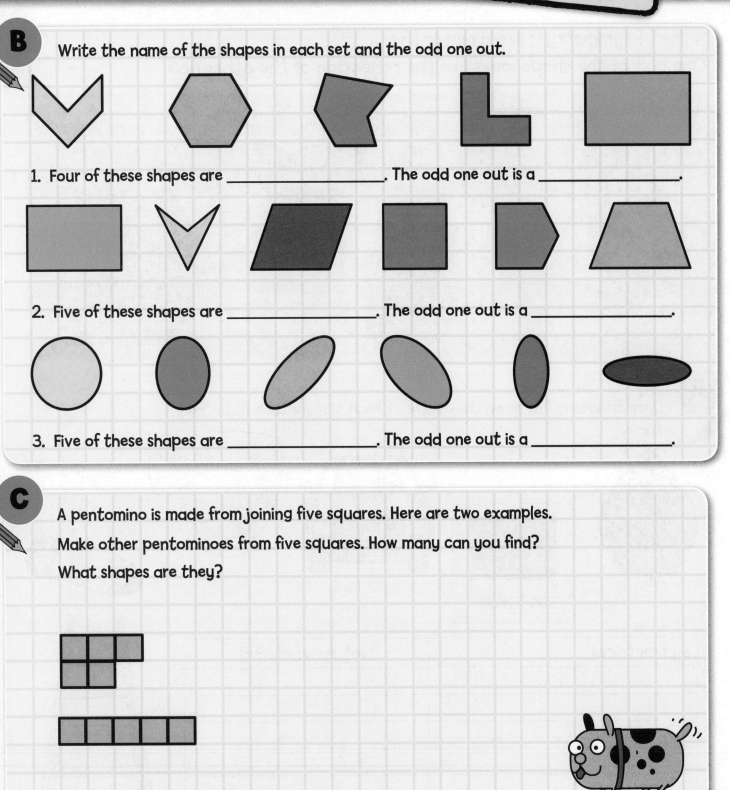

1. Four of these shapes are _____. The odd one out is a _____.

2. Five of these shapes are _____. The odd one out is a _____.

3. Five of these shapes are _____. The odd one out is a _____.

C A pentomino is made from joining five squares. Here are two examples.

Make other pentominoes from five squares. How many can you find?

What shapes are they?

Symmetry

Learning objective: to recognise and draw shapes with reflective symmetry

A line of symmetry is like a mirror line.
One half of the shape looks like the reflection of the other half.

Look at these lines of symmetry.

A

Draw a vertical line down the centre of each picture then fill in the table.

Symmetrical	Not symmetrical

DEFINITION

symmetry: When one half of a shape looks like an exact reflection of the other half.

B

Complete these drawings to make symmetrical shapes.

1.

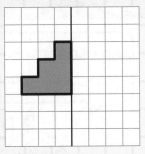

2.

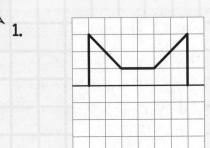

3.

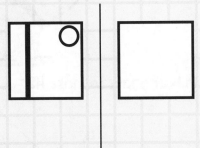

Now try to work out the mystery symmetry words below! Make up more mystery words of your own.

DECK, CODE, HOOD,

VHAT, TCV, HIN

C

Some letters of the alphabet and some numbers are symmetrical. Complete each of these letters and numbers.

1. M   2. D   3. V   4. J   5. ⊃

39

Angles

Learning objective: to use degrees to measure angles

We use degrees (°) to measure angles.

A $\frac{1}{4}$ turn is also called a right angle.
There are 90 degrees (90°) in a right angle.

A complete turn is the same as four right angles, or 360°.

A straight line is the same as two right angles, or 180°.

A

1. Take a piece of scrap paper.
2. Fold it to make a straight line.
3. Fold it again to make a right angle.

   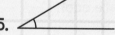

B

Estimate the size in degrees of each of these angles.

Use your folded right angle to help. (You can fold 90° in half again to make 45°.)

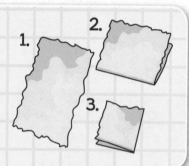

1.   2.   3.   4.

5.   6.   7.   8.

Complete the table to show your estimates.

Angle	1.	2.	3.	4.	5.	6.	7.	8.
Estimated size (°)								

40

angle: The space where two lines meet that measures how much one line turns away from the other.

C

Draw the right angles on these shapes. The first one has been done for you.

1.
2.
3.
4.
5.
6.

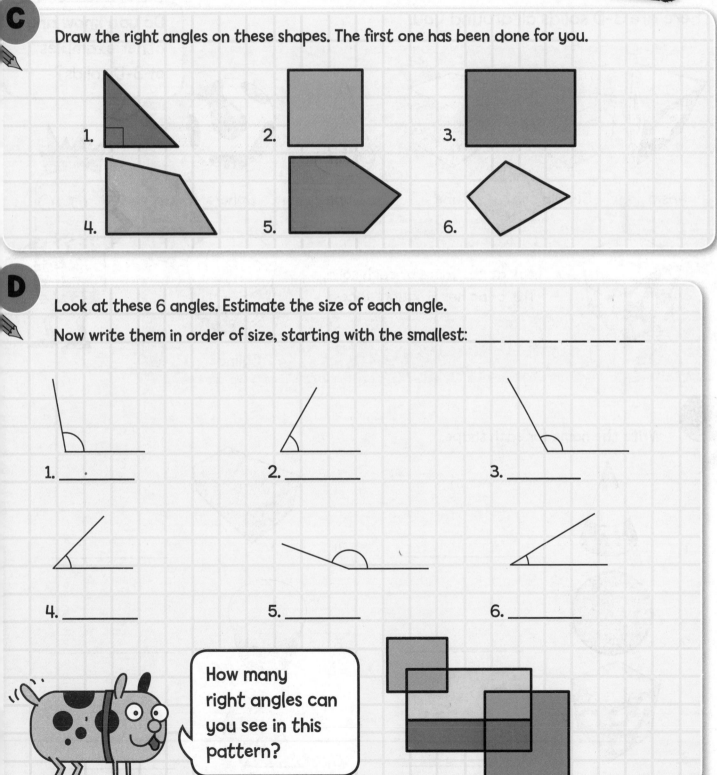

D

Look at these 6 angles. Estimate the size of each angle.

Now write them in order of size, starting with the smallest: ___ ___ ___ ___ ___ ___

1. ___.___
2. _____
3. _____
4. _____
5. _____
6. _____

How many right angles can you see in this pattern?

41

3-D solids

Learning objective: to name and describe 3-D solids

There are 3-D solids all around you.

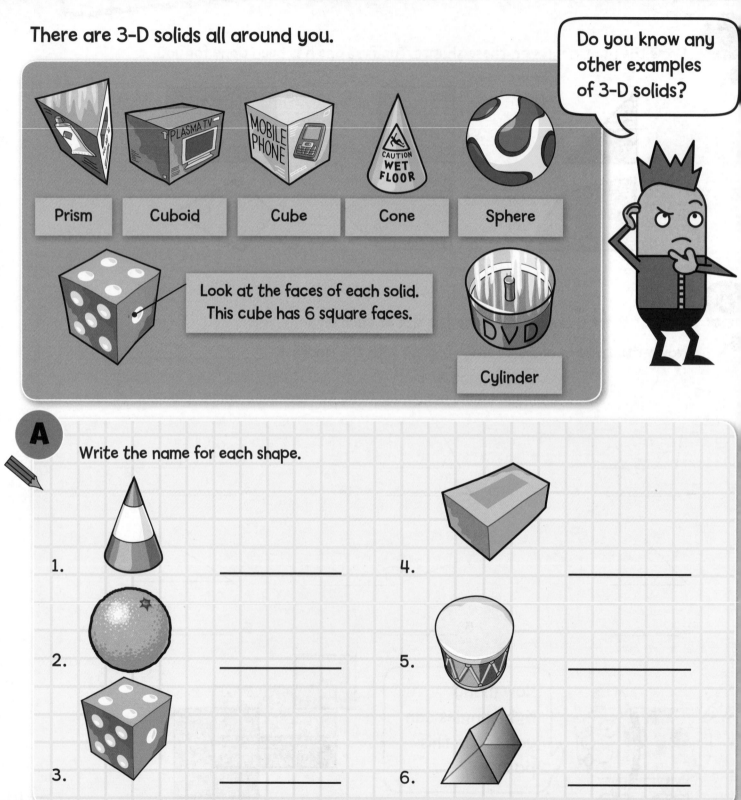

Do you know any other examples of 3-D solids?

Prism   Cuboid   Cube   Cone   Sphere

PLASMA TV   MOBILE PHONE   CAUTION WET FLOOR

Look at the faces of each solid. This cube has 6 square faces.

DVD

Cylinder

A Write the name for each shape.

1. _____

2. _____

3. _____

4. _____

5. _____

6. _____

DEFINITION

face: The flat surface of a solid shape is called a face.

B

Name the shapes in each set and find the odd one out.

1. Four of these shapes are _____.
    The odd one out is a _____.

2. Four of these shapes are _____.
    The odd one out is a _____.

3. Four of these shapes are _____.
    The odd one out is a _____.

C

Complete this chart.

Name of shape	cube	cuboid	prism
Total number of faces			
Number of square and rectangle faces			
Number of triangular faces			

D

Are these statements always, sometimes or never true?

1. A cuboid has a triangular face. _____
2. A cone has a circular face. _____
3. A cylinder has two circular faces of different sizes. _____
4. A prism has a square face.

_____

43

Measuring length

Learning objective: to read, estimate, measure and record using centimetres

A ruler is a useful tool for measuring smaller lengths.

This shows a centimetre ruler.

- Each division is 1 centimetre in length.
- Each small division between the centimetres is half a centimetre.
- The length of the stick is 6 centimetres, or 6cm.

DEFINITION

estimate: An estimate is a rough answer, without measuring.

A Look at the ruler above and estimate the length of each coloured line. Write your estimate in centimetres.

1. estimate: _____cm

2. estimate: _____cm

3. estimate: _____cm

4. estimate: _____cm

5. estimate: _____cm

6. estimate: _____cm

Take your best guess!

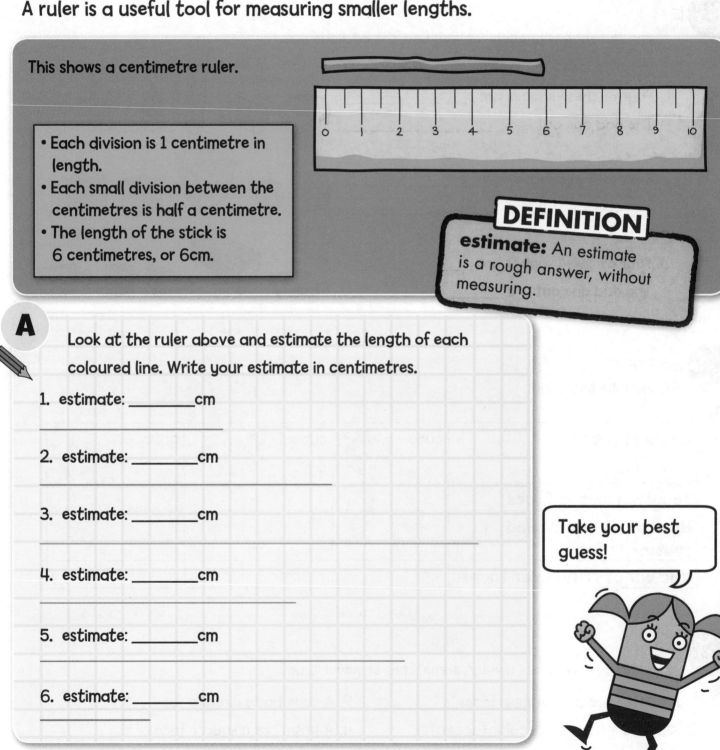

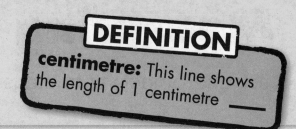

B

Use a ruler and measure the exact length of each line in Section A. Write each length in centimetres.

1. length: _____cm

2. length: _____cm

3. length: _____cm

4. length: _____cm

5. length: _____cm

6. length: _____cm

C

Measure each item and write the lengths.

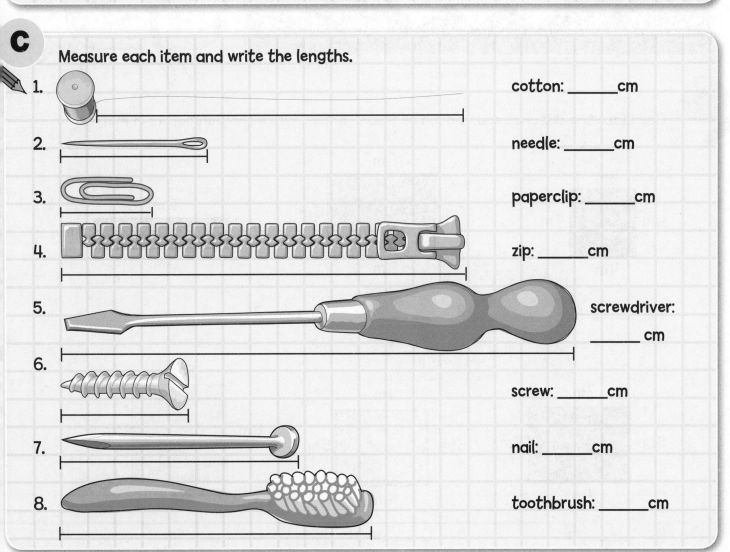

1. cotton: _____cm

2. needle: _____cm

3. paperclip: _____cm

4. zip: _____cm

5. screwdriver: _____ cm

6. screw: _____cm

7. nail: _____cm

8. toothbrush: _____cm

Measuring perimeter

Learning objective: to measure the perimeter of rectangles

The perimeter of a shape is the distance all around the edge.

This tile has a perimeter of 3cm + 3cm + 5cm + 5cm = 16cm

Use a ruler to check these measurements.

A

Calculate the distance round each of these shapes. Write the perimeters in metres.

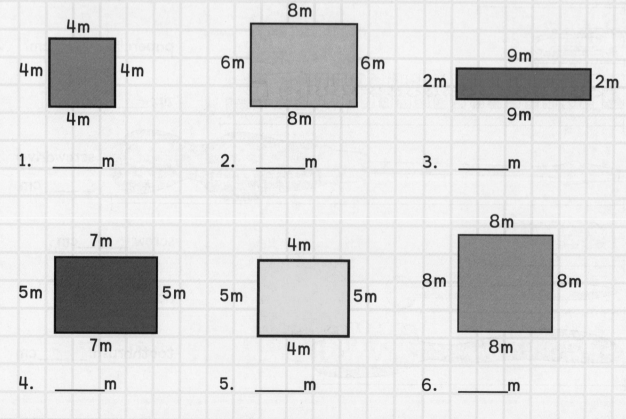

1. _____m

2. _____m

3. _____m

4. _____m

5. _____m

6. _____m

B

Use a ruler to measure the sides of each rectangle. Write the length, height and perimeter for these in centimetres.

1.

Length = _____cm

Height = _____cm

Perimeter = _____cm

2.

Length = _____cm

Height = _____cm

Perimeter = _____cm

3.

Length = _____cm

Height = _____cm

Perimeter = _____cm

4.

Length = _____cm

Height = _____cm

Perimeter = _____cm

5.

Length = _____cm

Height = _____cm

Perimeter = _____cm

6.

Length = _____cm

Height = _____cm

Perimeter = _____cm

C

Complete this chart. Write the length and height of each rectangle and calculate the perimeter.

1. 6m 2m

2. 8m 4m

3. 5m 5m

4. 7m 9m

5. 11m 1m

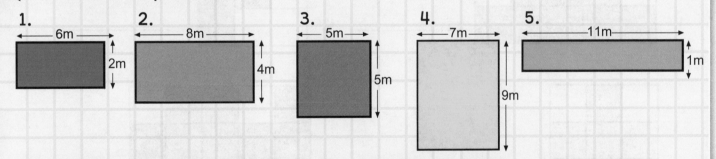

Rectangle	length	add	height	Multiply total by 2		Perimeter
1	6m	+	2m	=	8m → x 2	16m
2	m	+	m	=	m → x 2	m
3	m	+	m	=	m → x 2	m
4	m	+	m	=	m → x 2	m
5	m	+	m	=	m → x 2	m

Measuring area

Learning objective: to find the area of shapes on a square grid

To find the area of a shape you can draw it on a square grid and count the squares.

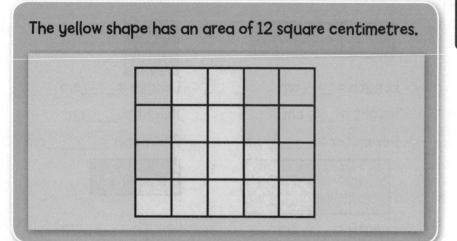

The yellow shape has an area of 12 square centimetres.

The side of each small square on this grid is 1cm.

A Count the squares and write the area of each shape.

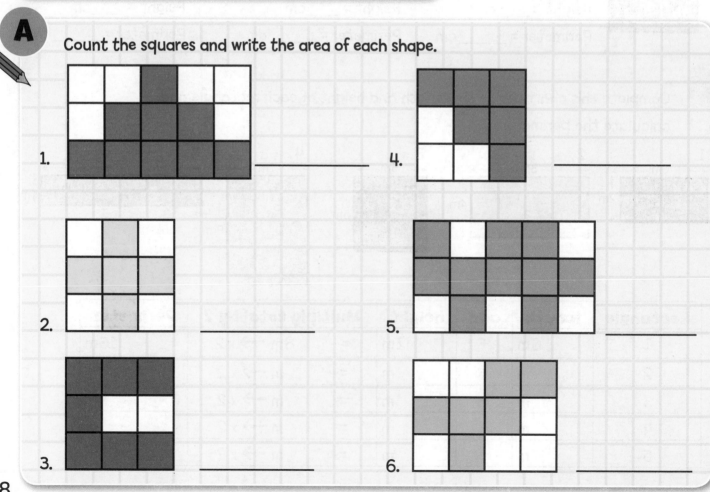

1. _____

2. _____

3. _____

4. _____

5. _____

6. _____

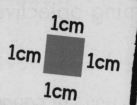
B

This plan shows the gardens of a hotel. Each square shows 1 square metre of ground. Count the squares and write the area for each section.

1. Area of swimming pool
= _____ square metres

2. Area of paths = _____ square metres

3. Area of car park = _____ square metres

4. Area of grass = _____ square metres

5. Area of flower border
= _____ square metres

C

A gardener is planning a path using 8 slabs. Each slab is 1 square metre. Here are two designs using 8 squares. Draw 3 more path designs using 8 squares.

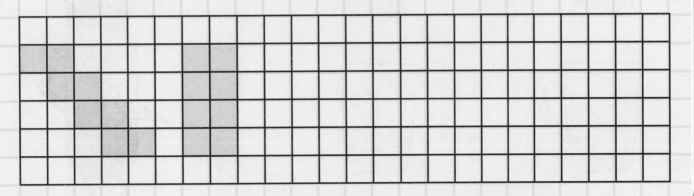

Measuring capacity

Learning objective: to read scales and use litres and millilitres

Metric units of capacity are litres (l) and millilitres (ml).

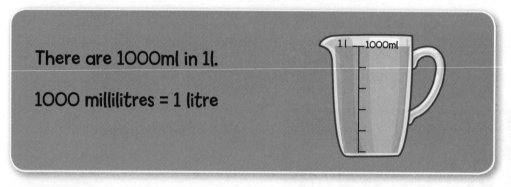

There are 1000ml in 1l.

1000 millilitres = 1 litre

A

Write the amount shown in each jug. Look carefully at the units of measurement for each jug.

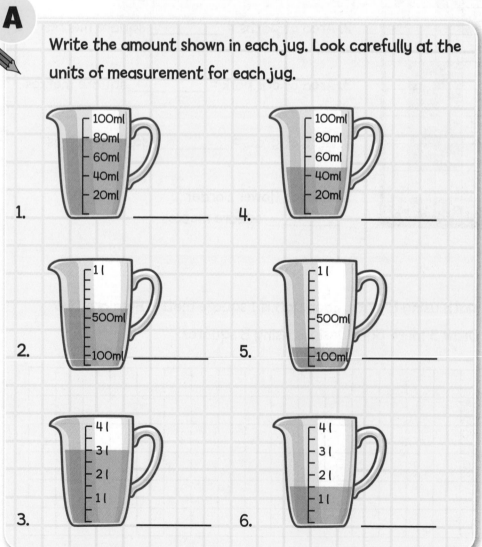

1. _____

2. _____

3. _____

4. _____

5. _____

6. _____

Amy filled a 17-litre tank using two different jugs. One jug held 3 litres and the other 4 litres. She used exactly 5 jugfuls to fill the tank. How many of each jug did she use?

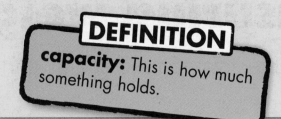

B

Each of these containers holds a different amount.

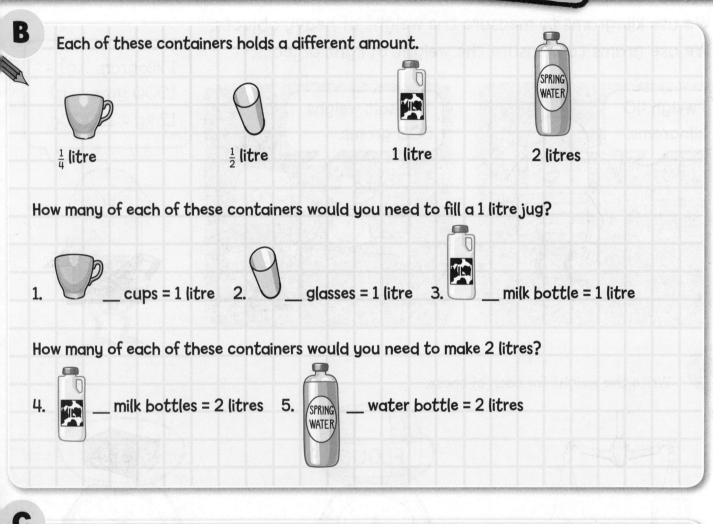

$\frac{1}{4}$ litre $\frac{1}{2}$ litre   1 litre   2 litres

How many of each of these containers would you need to fill a 1 litre jug?

1. __ cups = 1 litre   2. __ glasses = 1 litre   3. __ milk bottle = 1 litre

How many of each of these containers would you need to make 2 litres?

4. __ milk bottles = 2 litres   5. __ water bottle = 2 litres

C

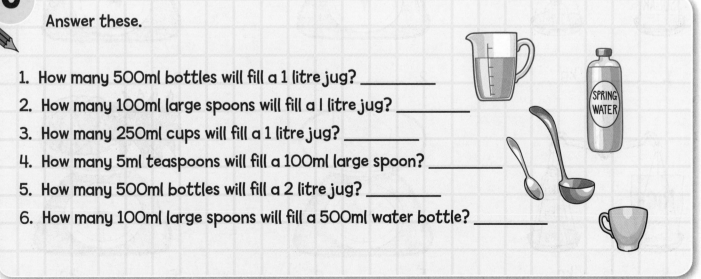

Answer these.

1. How many 500ml bottles will fill a 1 litre jug? _____
2. How many 100ml large spoons will fill a 1 litre jug? _____
3. How many 250ml cups will fill a 1 litre jug? _____
4. How many 5ml teaspoons will fill a 100ml large spoon? _____
5. How many 500ml bottles will fill a 2 litre jug? _____
6. How many 100ml large spoons will fill a 500ml water bottle? _____

Measuring weight

We use kilograms to measure the weight of heavy objects.
We use grams to measure the weight of light objects.

I weigh 40 kilograms.

This salt weighs 500 grams.

1 kilogram (kg) = 1000 grams (g)
12 kg = 12000g

A Write the weight for each of these.

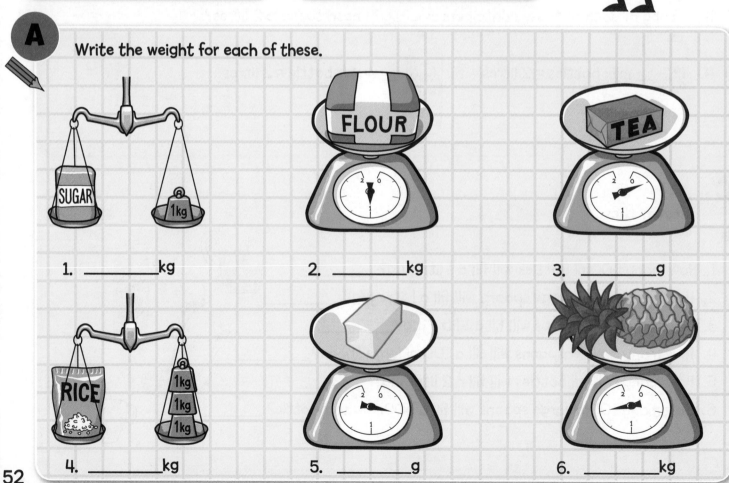

1. _____ kg

2. _____ kg

3. _____ g

4. _____ kg

5. _____ g

6. _____ kg

52

B Convert these measures.

1. 2000g = _____ kg

2. 5kg = _____ g

3. 4000g = _____ kg

4. 6kg = _____ g

5. 9kg = _____ g

6. 3000g = _____ kg

These shapes weigh 18kg altogether. If each pyramid weighs 3kg, what is the weight of each cube?

C Write the weight of each bag to the nearest $\frac{1}{2}$kg.

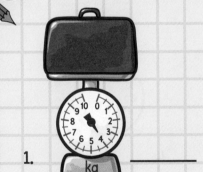

1. kg _____

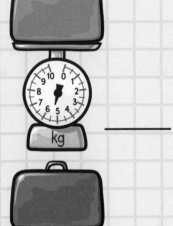

2. kg _____

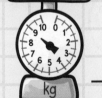

3. kg _____

4. kg _____

5. kg _____

6. kg _____

Time

Learning objective: to read the time to the nearest 5 minutes

There are 60 minutes in 1 hour. It takes 5 minutes for the minute hand to move from one marker to the next.

This shows the hour. It is past 3 o'clock.

I wonder how long it will take you to complete this page?

This shows the number of minutes past the hour.
It is 40 minutes past 3 or 3.40.

A

Write these times.

1. _____   2. _____   3. _____   4. _____

5. _____   6. _____   7. _____   8. _____

B

Read these time problems. Write the answers.

1. A TV programme starts at 6.15 and lasts for half an hour.

   What time will it end?   _____

2. Nathan gets up at 7 o'clock and leaves for school an hour later.

   What time does he leave for school?   _____

3. A boat leaves at ten past one and returns at half-past one.

   How long is the boat at sea?   _____

4. A cake takes 25 minutes to bake. It was put in the oven at 4 o'clock.

   When will it be ready?   _____

5. Gemma is playing at the park. It is quarter to 12. She has to go home at 12.30.

   How much longer does she have to play?   _____

C

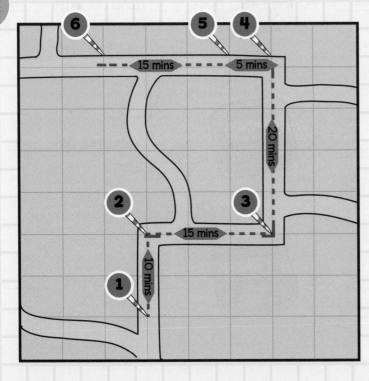

Look at the map showing the length of time a bus takes between each stop. Complete this bus timetable. Work out the time the bus will be at each stop.

Bus Stop	Time
1	9:05
2	
3	
4	
5	
6	

55

More time

This is a digital clock.

This is the hour. → 8:28

These are the minutes.

My digital clock has told me I'm going to be late for school!

A Write these times.

1. 7:03 _____ minutes past _____

2. 3:11 _____ minutes past _____

3. 1:57 _____ minutes to _____

4. 2:40 _____ minutes to _____

5. 9:22 _____ minutes past _____

6. 4:25 _____ minutes past _____

7. 12:50 _____ minutes to _____

8. 5:55 _____ minutes to _____

B The bus takes 12 minutes to get to each stop. Write the missing times on the timetable. Then calculate the answers to the questions.

Bus station	8:12
School	8:24
Train station	
Sports centre	
Supermarket	

1. How long does it take to get from the bus station to these places?

    Sports centre   ____ minutes

    Supermarket   ____ minutes

2. How much farther in minutes is the supermarket from the school?

    _____ minutes

Both of these clocks tell the same time. However, one has Roman numerals instead of the numbers 1-12.

It's 2 o'clock!

C Write these times.

1. _____ o'clock

2. _____ minutes to _____

3. _____ minutes to _____

4. _____ minutes past _____

5. _____ minutes past _____

6. _____ minutes past _____

Handling data

Learning objective: to read the data in bar graphs

Data is information that has been collected.

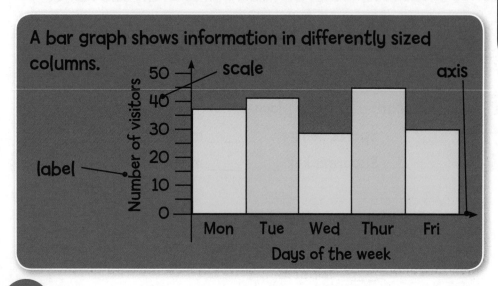

A bar graph shows information in differently sized columns.

Bar graphs look like bars. What do you think pie charts look like?

A

Answer these questions about the bar graph.

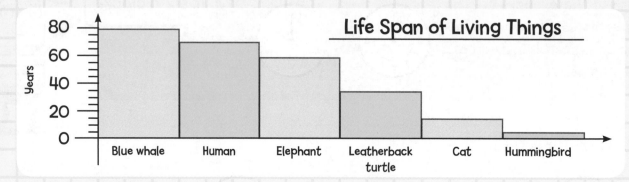

Life Span of Living Things

1. What has a life span of 70 years? _____

2. What has the longest life span? _____

3. What has the shortest life span? _____

4. How long might a leatherback turtle live? _____

5. What has a life span of about 15 years? _____

6. How much longer is a blue whale expected to live than a human? _____

7. What is expected to live 20 years more than a cat? _____

8. What creatures are expected to live longer than 50 years? _____
_____

B

This chart shows the favourite fruits of children in Class 3.

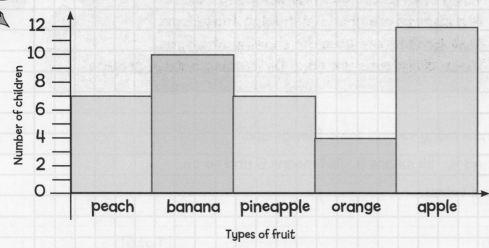

Take the difference between the number of children who liked oranges and those who liked peaches. Add that to the number who liked pineapple. That will give the number of people who liked my favourite fruit!

1. How many children chose bananas as their favourite fruit?

_____ children

2. Which type of fruit did 12 children choose as their favourite?

_____

3. Which fruit did the least number of children choose? _____

4. How many children chose peaches as their favourite fruit?

_____ children

5. How many children altogether chose bananas or pineapples?

_____ children

6. How many more children liked apples than bananas?

_____ more children

7. Which two fruits did the same number of children choose?

_____ and _____

8. Which are the two most popular fruits?

_____ and _____

9. How many more children liked bananas than oranges?

_____ more children

Graphs and charts

Learning objective: to use different types of graph and chart

We use different graphs and charts for different jobs.

Tally charts are good for **keeping count**.
Pie charts are good for showing **fractions**.
Line graphs are good for showing **changes**.
Venn diagrams are good for putting data in **groups**.

A

This tally chart shows how many sweets some friends ate.

I, II, III and IIII mean 1, 2, 3 and 4. IIII means 5, IIII I means 6 and so on.

Put in the missing tallies and totals.

Name	Tally	Total
Jack	IIII III	8
Claire	IIII IIII IIII IIII IIII IIII II	
Freddy		16
Anya	IIII III	

This pie chart shows the fraction of sweets eaten by each friend.

Put Anya's and Freddy's names on the chart. Circle the right answer.

1. Claire ate half the sweets.

   TRUE / FALSE.

2. Jack ate more than Anya.

   TRUE / FALSE

3. Freddy ate a quarter of the sweets.

   TRUE / FALSE

4. Anya ate twice as many sweets as Freddy.

   TRUE / FALSE

5. Freddy ate half as many sweets as Claire.

   TRUE / FALSE.

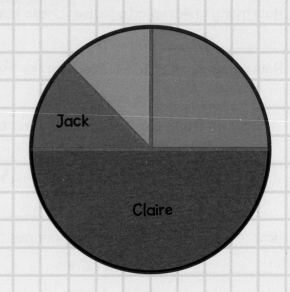

DEFINITION

graph: A mathematical drawing that shows data.

B

Jenny nibbled a chocolate bar.

This line graph shows how quickly she ate it.

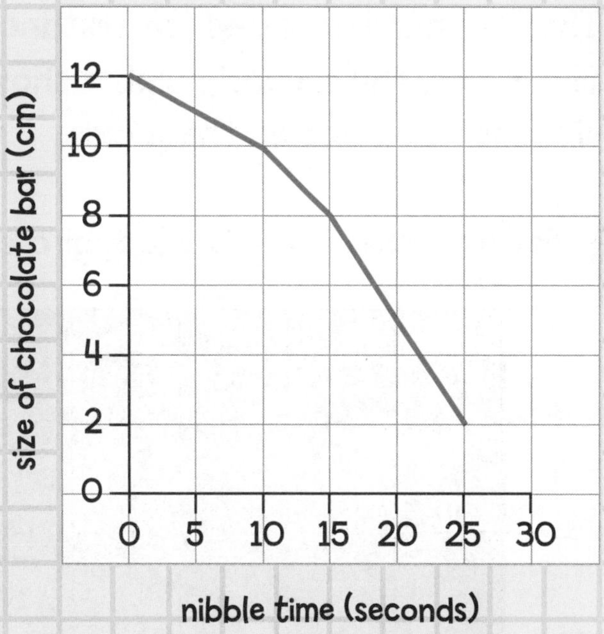

1. How much of the bar was left after 15 seconds? ________
2. How much of the bar was left after 20 seconds? ________
3. Does Jenny's nibbling speed up or slow down? ________
4. If Jenny keeps nibbling at this speed, can she finish the bar in less than 30 seconds? ________

C

This Venn diagram shows the ice creams that different people liked. Where the circles overlap, people liked more than one kind of ice cream.

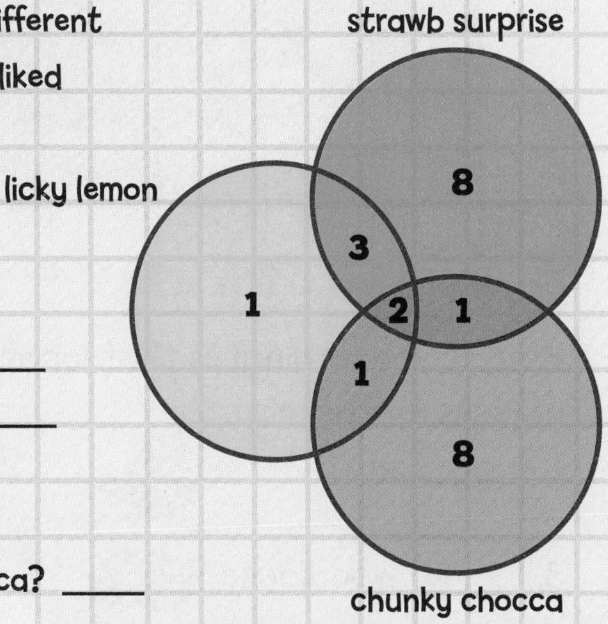

1. How many people liked only licky lemon? _____
2. How many people liked all three ice creams? _____
3. How many people liked only strawb surprise? _____
4. How many people liked chunky chocca and strawb surprise, but not licky lemon? _____
5. How many people altogether liked chunky chocca? _____

Coordinates

Learning objective: to know how to use coordinates

x comes before y in the alphabet, so we read the x axis first then the y axis.

Coordinates are pairs of numbers that point to an exact position.

The first number shows the distance along the **x** axis. The second number shows the distance up or down the **y** axis.

A For example: There is a ladybird at location (7, 5) on this map of a garden.

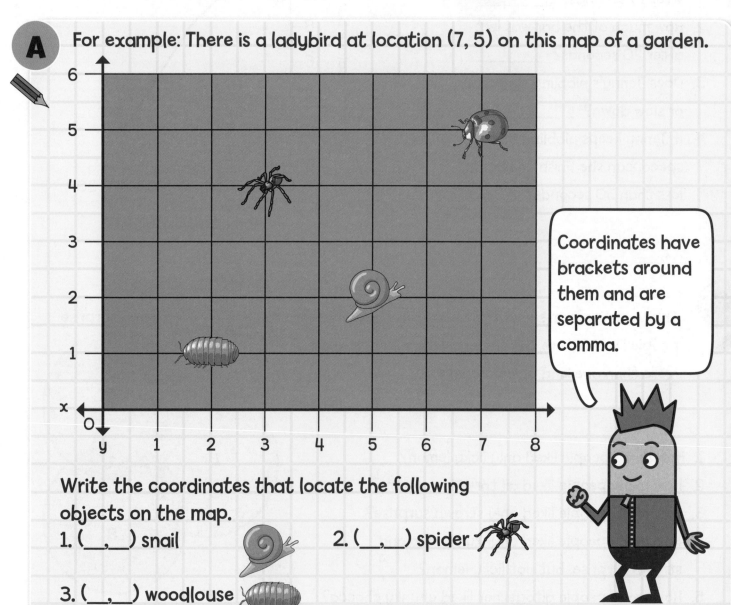

Coordinates have brackets around them and are separated by a comma.

Write the coordinates that locate the following objects on the map.

1. (__,__) snail

2. (__,__) spider

3. (__,__) woodlouse

B

Collect all the buried coins by writing the coordinates for each of them.

A (__,__)   E (__,__)

B (__,__)   F (__,__)

C (__,__)   G (__,__)

D (__,__)   H (__,__)

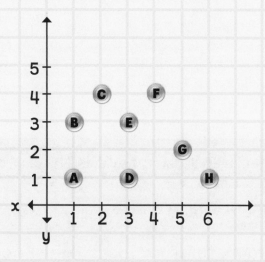

C

Coordinates can also use negative numbers. Write the coordinates of the corners of this square in the spaces on the grid. The first one has been done for you.

Look how the number lines on the x and y axes go down to zero and then change to negative numbers.

1. (-3, 3)   2. (__,__)

3. (__,__)   4. (__,__)

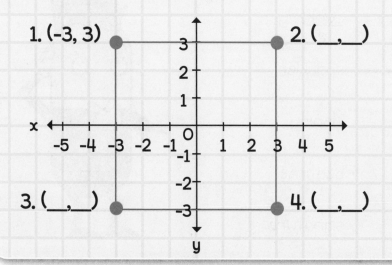

63

Spelling skills

Learning objective: to learn different spelling methods

One way of learning to spell a new word is by using these 5 steps.

1. Look at the word
2. Say it
3. Cover it
4. Write it
5. Check it

Look for common letter patterns to spell these groups of words.

could, should, would	found, ground, loud, shout
clown, frown, town	coin, noise, soil, voice
bridge, fudge, hedge	cuddle, middle, little, table

A Sometimes you can find a root word or a word within a word.

Underline the root word in each of these groups of words.

<u>cook</u>	<u>cook</u>er	<u>cook</u>ery
spark	sparkle	sparkler
clear	cleared	clearly
bedroom	bedstead	bedtime
sign	signal	signature

B

Homophones are tricky words that sound the same but are spelled differently.

Write the correct homophone in each space below.

> **hear** or **here**　　**ate** or **eight**
>
> **right** or **write**　　**beech** or **beach**
>
> **would** or **wood**　　**where**, **were** or **wear**

1. Teri is nearly _____ years old.
2. I couldn't _____ what she said.
3. I don't know if it's the _____ way.
4. _____ you like to sleep over at my house?
5. _____ can I get the bus into town?
6. We made sandcastles on the _____ .

List any other homophones that you know:

DEFINITION

mnemonic: A picture or a clue to help you remember how to spell tricky words.

This is an example of a mnemonic; this **hear** has an **ear** in it!

65

Nouns and plurals

Learning objective: to learn plural forms of words

A noun is a person, a place or a thing. Nouns can be singular (only one) or plural (more than one).

A

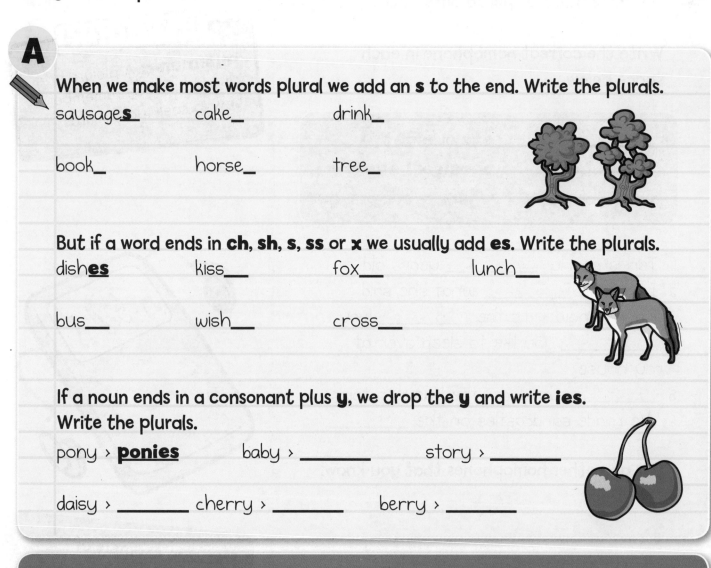

When we make most words plural we add an **s** to the end. Write the plurals.

sausage**s**   cake_   drink_

book_   horse_   tree_

But if a word ends in **ch**, **sh**, **s**, **ss** or **x** we usually add **es**. Write the plurals.

dish**es**   kiss__   fox__   lunch__

bus__   wish__   cross__

If a noun ends in a consonant plus **y**, we drop the **y** and write **ies**. Write the plurals.

pony > **ponies**   baby > _____   story > _____

daisy > _____   cherry > _____   berry > _____

Some tricky plurals don't follow the rules. Learn them by heart.

man > men   child > children   leaf > leaves
mouse > mice   goose > geese   person > people

DEFINITION

vowels: a, e, i, o and u.
consonants: b, c, d, f, g, h, j, k, l, m, n, p, q, r, s, t, v, w, x, y, z.

B

Read the poem below and turn the singular nouns into plurals. Mostly you can just add **s** but sometimes you have to rewrite the word in the space.

I Love the Seasons

I love it in the spring when the **bud__** burst into **million__** of tiny **flower__** .

I love it in the summer when we can make **sandcastle__** on the beach.

I love it in the autumn when the **leaf** _____ on the **tree__** turn from green to gold.

Best of all, I love it in the winter when we can make **snowman** _____ .

The words **sheep**, **deer** and **fish** stay the same whether they are singular or plural.

C

Change the nouns in bold in these sentences to plurals.

1. There is a **mouse** in the house! › There are _____ in the house!

2. There was only one **loaf**.   › There were only two _____ .

3. We saw a **goose** in the park. › We saw _____ in the park.

67

Prefixes and suffixes

Learning objective: to learn common prefixes and suffixes

Prefixes are extra letters added to the beginning of words.
They change the meaning of the root word.

For example:

The rabbit appeared, then **dis**appeared, then **re**appeared!

A

Writing **un** at the beginning of these words will change their meaning. Try it and see!

untie   ___fair

___lock   ___do

___like   ___lucky

___likely   ___happy

___able   ___hurt

Choose three words from the lists above to complete the dialogue below.
Write the words in the spaces.

Tom's mum: I'm very _____ with you.

Tom: It's so _____ ! It wasn't my fault.

I'm just _____ !

DEFINITION

prefixes: The extra letters added to the beginning of a word.

suffixes: The extra letters added to the end of a word.

B

Underline words with prefixes in this passage. Look for **dis, re, im, un.**

Tom and Jez went to see a remake of *Monsters of the Deep.* Writing about it in a movie review for their school magazine, they said, "The monsters were unrealistic and unimaginative really. There was lots of action but the plot was disjointed and impossible to follow."

Suffixes are extra letters added to the end of words. Look at how they change the meaning of the root word.

The word unsuccessful has a prefix *and* a suffix!

For example:

hope > hopeless > hopeful   care > careful > careless

use > useful > useless   thought > thoughtful > thoughtless

C

Choose a suffix to make sense of these sentences.
Write **less** or **ful.**

1. It was very thought_____ of Jenny to buy flowers.
2. The toy was use_____ without a battery.
3. I felt hope_____ at the start but then everything went wrong!
4. I knew I had to be care_____ this time.

Commas, questions, exclamations

Learning objective: to learn basic punctuation

Commas tell readers to pause and take a moment to understand what a sentence is about.

- Put a comma after each item of a list.
- Never put a comma before the word 'and'.
- Put a comma after a group of words that belong together.

How to use commas:
- After each item in a list.
- To separate ideas within a sentence.

For example:

The huge plate was piled high with bacon, egg, mushrooms, fried onions, black pudding, baked beans and tomato!

A

Write the commas in these sentences.

1. We'll have two cornets with raspberry sauce a vanilla ice cream a carton of orange juice and a cup of tea please.

2. I'd like to order the tomato soup an egg and cress sandwich a banana smoothie and a chocolate muffin please.

3. The cat ran up the stairs down the corridor through the classroom and into Mrs Lane's office!

4. Go right at the lights turn right again at the T-junction then first left.

5. The children bought a ball a notebook a pencil case and some balloons.

Sentences that ask questions usually begin with What, When, Where, Why or How.

Exclamation marks (!) show surprise or excitement.
Question marks (?) are used at the end of sentences when a question is asked.

B

Read the sentences below and decide whether to write an exclamation mark or a question mark in each one.

1. Suddenly, all the lights went out__
2. "Aaaaaaaargh__" he cried.
3. Gina called out, "Hey, Tom__"
4. "What are 'gators__" she asked.
5. How do we know there's no life on Mars__

C

Write 2 sentences with an exclamation mark at the end of each one.

D

Write 2 sentences with a question mark at the end of each one.

Inverted commas

Learning objective: to learn how to use inverted commas

Inverted commas are drawn around the exact words that are spoken.
This is called direct speech.

For example:

"How many children are coming?" asked Jason.

How to use inverted commas:
- Open the inverted commas at the start and close them at the end of the words spoken.
- All other punctuation goes inside the inverted commas.

A Write the missing inverted commas in the sentences below.

1. Tara cried, Wait for me!
2. Do you think he's an elf? asked Taylor.
3. Okay, said Sharon. What's wrong?
4. Wow! said Zac. You're a genius!

Inverted commas are sometimes called speech marks.

B Write the missing inverted commas in this story.

Ali and Bansi were in the Spooky Maize Maze.
    I think we must be lost, said Bansi, because I remember this path.
    A ghostly cry came from behind the hedge: Wooooh, wooooooh!
    Stop scaring me, said Ali.
    It's not me! replied Bansi.
    Help! they both cried.

Direct speech can come at either the beginning or the end of a sentence.

> **For example:** "I'm only joking," Max said.   Max said, "I'm only joking."
>
> Because the words complete the sentence a full stop is needed.

C Rewrite this sentence to put the direct speech at the end.

"These cakes are delicious," said the chef.

D Rewrite this sentence to put the direct speech at the beginning.

The vet said, "Dogs need a healthy diet."

Indirect (reported) speech does not need inverted commas.

> **For example:**
>
> Mira said that she would go. ⟶ Mira said, "I will go."
>
> Indirect speech ⟶ Direct speech

Look at the way the pronouns (she/I) and verbs (would/will) change in the example.

E Use the example above to help you rewrite this indirect speech as direct speech.

1. Lauren said she felt ill.

2. Sam said it wasn't fair.

Apostrophes

Learning objective: to learn to use apostrophes

Apostrophes can shorten words or tell you to whom something belongs.

An apostrophe can replace missing letters:

For example:

do not ➜ don't	it is ➜ it's
we are ➜ we're	they will ➜ they'll

Apostrophes are tricky! Keep practising until you understand how they work.

A Shorten these words by using apostrophes.

1. cannot → **can't**
2. should not →_____
3. they will →_____
4. she is →_____
5. could not →_____
6. we will →_____
7. where is _____
8. they are →_____

Apostrophes can also show possession.

For example: Ben's shoes.

B Rewrite each of these phrases using an apostrophe.

1. The shoes belonging to Ben **Ben's shoes**_____
2. The book belonging to my friend _____
3. The lead belonging to the dog _____
4. The car belonging to Joe _____
5. The whiskers belonging to the cat _____

The possessive apostrophe can also tell you how many there are.

For example:

1. The boy's trainers were new. (one boy)
2. The boys' trainers were new. (more than one boy)

Remember these exceptions – the children's clothes, the men's clothes, the people's clothes.

If the noun is singular the apostrophe goes before the s.
If the noun is plural the apostrophe goes after the s.

C

Rewrite each of these phrases using a possessive apostrophe.

1. The cat belonging to the girl.

   The girl's cat

2. The book belonging to the teacher.

3. The television belonging to the family.

4. The red nose belonging to the clown.

5. The pram belonging to the baby.

6. The house belonging to the dolls.

7. The drawings belonging to the children.

8. The race belonging to the men.

DEFINITION

To 'possess' means to 'own'.
possessive apostrophes: These are used to show who owns a particular thing.

Nouns, pronouns, connectives

Learning objective: to recognise nouns, pronouns, connectives

A noun is a naming word. It can be a person, place or thing.

For example:

| The bee buzzed. **bee** is a noun. | Richard ran away. **Richard** is a noun. | The cats miaowed loudly. **cats** is a noun. |

A Underline the nouns in these sentences:

1. The flowers were pretty.   2. I live in London.   3. The food was delicious.
4. Zak was asleep.   5. The girls laughed.   6. My sister has a laptop.

A pronoun is a word you can use to replace a noun so that you don't have to repeat it.

For example: Connor is kind. > He is kind.   **He** is a pronoun.

B Rewrite these sentences using pronouns.

Choose from this list: him   she   it   they   them   we

1. The flowers were pretty so I put the flowers in a Vase.
   The flowers were pretty so I put <u>them</u> in a vase.

2. Zak was asleep and I didn't want to wake Zak up.

3. I like London because London has an interesting history.

4. The girls laughed because the girls thought it was funny.

5. Chris and I went swimming. Chris and I had a great time.

DEFINITION

Noun: A person, a place or a thing.
Pronoun: A word you can use instead of the noun.
Connective: A word that links ideas, sentences and paragraphs together.

Connectives are words that link ideas, sentences and paragraphs. Here are some useful connectives:

first, next, finally, consequently, later, suddenly, except, meanwhile, however, when, but, before, and, after, although, also, then

C

Choose connectives from the list above to complete this school diary.

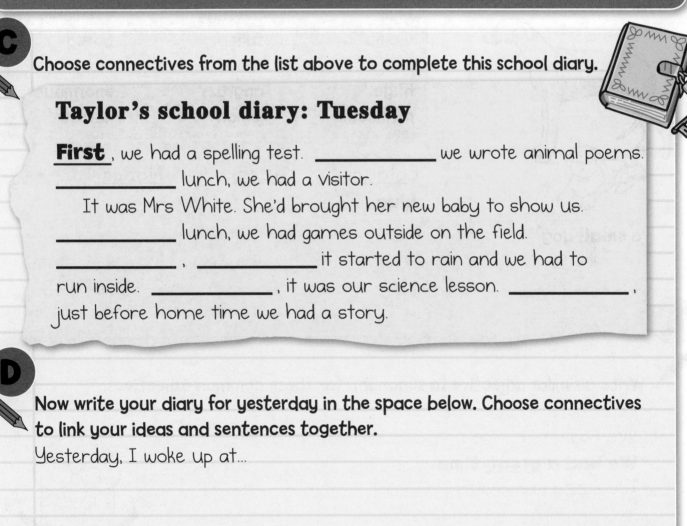

Taylor's school diary: Tuesday

First , we had a spelling test. _____ we wrote animal poems. _____ lunch, we had a visitor.

It was Mrs White. She'd brought her new baby to show us. _____ lunch, we had games outside on the field.

_____ , _____ it started to rain and we had to run inside. _____ , it was our science lesson. _____ , just before home time we had a story.

D

Now write your diary for yesterday in the space below. Choose connectives to link your ideas and sentences together.

Yesterday, I woke up at...

Adjectives

Learning objective: to learn to use adjectives

Adjectives are used to describe people, places or things.

For example:

a large dog

a small dog

A Sort these adjectives into three groups.
Write them below each group heading.

blue	average	excitable
violet	sullen	bored
indigo	raucous	scarlet
huge	angry	enormous
minuscule	lemon	narrow

Colours: Sizes: Moods:
blue

B

Write a similar adjective (a synonym) for these common adjectives.

1. We had a nice time.
   We had a <u>great</u> time.
2. The pizza was okay.

3. The giant stomped his big foot.

4. It was a funny movie.

This activity is the opposite of difficult. It's easy!

Opposite adjectives are known as antonyms.

C Write an antonym for each of these adjectives.

black › **white**

bold › _____

hazy › _____

hairy › _____

unusual › _____

scorching › _____

expensive › _____

popular › _____

delicious › _____

polite › _____

D Change these adjectives to alter the meaning of the sentences.

1. A friendly, little dog came bounding up to her.

   A _____, _____ dog came bounding up to her.

2. It was an antique table.

   It was a _____ table.

3. It was a difficult job.

   It was an _____ job.

4. He was in a happy mood.

   He was in a _____ mood.

5. She went red when she saw him.

   She went _____ when she saw him.

DEFINITION

synonym: A word with a similar meaning.
antonym: A word with an opposite meaning.

Fronted adverbials

Learning objective: to know how to write a fronted adverbial

Fronted adverbials are used to emphasise when, where and how an action takes place. They are written at the front of the sentence.

How to use fronted adverbials:
- A comma is written after the fronted adverbial.
- An adverbial can be a single word, a phrase or a clause.

For example:
Look at how using fronted adverbials changes these sentences. The fronted adverbials are underlined.

They were tired at the end of the race.
↓
At the end of the race, they were tired.

The turtle slowly crawled out of the ocean.
↓
Slowly, the turtle crawled out of the ocean.

There were butterflies everywhere she looked.
↓
Everywhere she looked, there were butterflies.

A Underline the fronted adverbials in these sentences.

1. In the end, they were happy.
2. Carefully, she crossed the stream.
3. Back at the house, there was no one home.
4. When the bell rang, they ran outside to play.

B

Insert the missing commas after the fronted adverbials in these sentences.

1. In the morning it was sunny.
2. As it turned out they were lucky.
3. When the audience cheered they took a bow.
4. Later that day the storm broke.

C

Draw lines to join these fronted adverbials to the correct endings.

1. On Saturday,   there was a tree house.
2. In the middle of the wood,   she went to Australia.
3. The following year,   the weekend begins.

D

Rewrite the words in these sentences by moving the adverbials to the front. The first one has been done for you.

Don't forget to put capital letters, commas and full stops in the right places.

1. It went dark suddenly.
   Suddenly, it went dark.
2. She went to a friend's house after school.

3. The team lost every match before Marek joined them.

4. They sang 'Happy Birthday' when the candles were lit.

81

Tenses

Learning objective: to understand different tenses

The tense of the verbs in a sentence tells you when something happens.

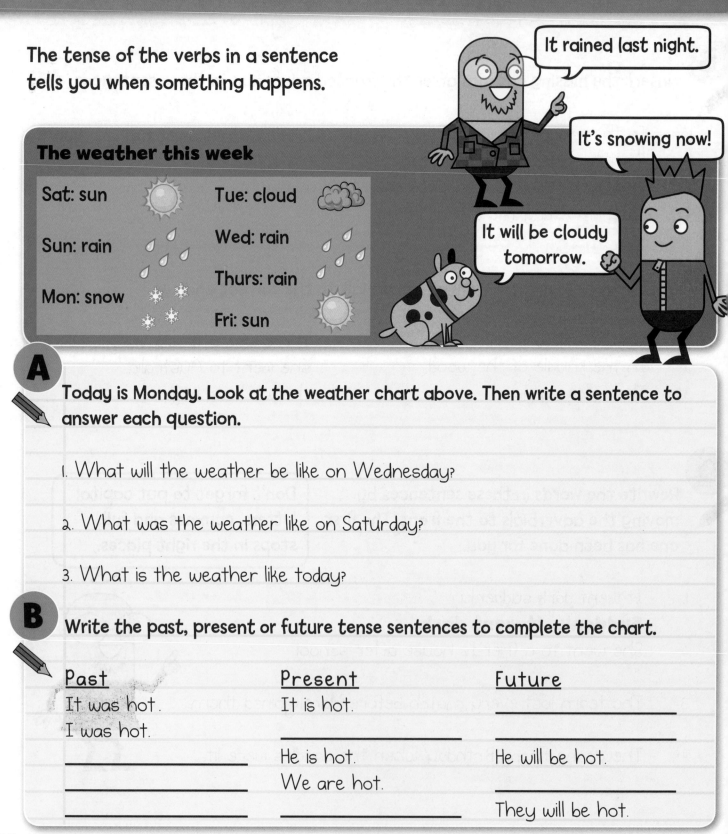

It rained last night.

It's snowing now!

It will be cloudy tomorrow.

The weather this week

Sat: sun

Sun: rain

Mon: snow

Tue: cloud

Wed: rain

Thurs: rain

Fri: sun

A

Today is Monday. Look at the weather chart above. Then write a sentence to answer each question.

1. What will the weather be like on Wednesday?

2. What was the weather like on Saturday?

3. What is the weather like today?

B

Write the past, present or future tense sentences to complete the chart.

Past	Present	Future
It was hot.	It is hot.	_____
I was hot.	_____	_____
_____	He is hot.	He will be hot.
_____	We are hot.	_____
_____	_____	They will be hot.

To find out more about suffixes turn to page 68.

A suffix can change the time from the present to the past:

Present	Present continuous	Past	Present perfect
I play.	I am playing.	I played.	I have played.
I work.	I am working.	I worked.	I have worked.

C

Complete these present and past tense verbs.

Present	Present continuous	Past	Present perfect
I paint.	I am paint____.	I paint____.	I _____ painted.
I jump.	I am jump____.	I jump____.	I _____ jumped.
I shop.	I am shop____.	I shop____.	I _____ shopped.
I skip.	I am skip____.	I skip____.	I _____ skipped.

Irregular verbs don't follow the usual rules.
Learn them by heart.

Present	Past
I get	I got
I have	I had
I go	I went

D

Change the verbs in this story from the present tense to the past tense.

I get out of the car and step in a puddle. We hear the band playing. They have started already! I run all the way to the hall.

I ____ out of the car and _____ in a puddle. We ____ the band playing. They ___ started already! I ____ all the way to the hall.

Paragraphs

Learning objective: to know how to write a paragraph

A paragraph is a piece of writing that focuses on one idea. It starts on a new line and sometimes has an indent or a number.

For example:

Sharks are my favourite animal. They have lived on Earth for over 400 million years. The most interesting thing about sharks is their teeth. They have thousands of them, set in rows, so when they lose a tooth another one moves forward to takes its place.

I wrote this paragraph about my favourite animal.

A Read the paragraph below, which talks about people's fear of sharks. Cross out the sentence that doesn't belong in this paragraph.

People are afraid of sharks but not all sharks are fierce. Many sharks are harmless to humans. The hammerhead shark has eyes on the sides of its head! In fact, more people die from bee stings than from shark attacks.

B Write a paragraph about your favourite animal.
Try to write at least three sentences.

Your first sentence should tell the reader what the paragraph is about.

To find out more about direct speech turn to page 72.

When you are writing direct speech, you start a new paragraph each time a new speaker starts.

For example:

"What would your superhero power be?" asked the teacher.

"I would like a super brain," Amir replied, "then I could solve all the world's problems."

C

What superpowers do you think the other children in the class would like? Write what you think Flo and Jacob said in the gaps.

"What would your superhero power be?" the teacher asked Flo and Jacob.

"_____," Flo said,

"_____."

"_____," said Jacob,

"_____."

D

The first part of each paragraph below is missing. Write the missing words. Choose from the following paragraph beginnings:

I would like x-ray vision
I would like to be able to change the weather

"_____," said

Raj, "then we could have snowball fights in summer."

"_____," said Katja, "then

I could find all the things I've lost in my bedroom."

Clauses

Learning objective: to know the difference between a main clause and a subordinate clause

A main clause is a group of words that makes sense by itself. A subordinate clause does not make sense by itself. It needs the main clause.

For example:

I love bones.
↑
Main clause

I love bones because I am a dog.
↑   ↑
Main clause   Subordinate clause

How to use subordinate clauses:
- A subordinate clause can go at the beginning of a sentence or later in a sentence.
- A subordinate clause begins with a conjunction (e.g. but, when, because, since, although, while, unless, after).

A

Underline the subordinate clauses.

1. When I am older, I want to be an astronaut.
2. I must have grown, because these trousers are too short.
3. I'll meet you, after I've had lunch.
4. I said I was sorry, although it was an accident.

A subordinate clause is sometimes called a dependent clause.

B

Underline the main clauses.

1. When I was six, I had a party.
2. I clean my teeth before I go to bed.
3. Unless it's raining, we're having a picnic.
4. While the cat's away, the mice will play!

Remember!
A main clause could make a sentence by itself.

I love chasing cats!
(That's a main clause.)

C

Write the missing conjunctions in the spaces. Choose from the list. Then underline the subordinate clauses.

while   **unless**   **if**   **before**

1. _____ you have a better idea, let's go to the cinema.
2. I would buy them, _____ you like them.
3. Stop, _____ going any further!
4. You can play in the garden, _____ I cook dinner.

D

Draw lines to join the main clauses and the subordinate clauses together.

Main clause	Subordinate clause
Run home	until it sets.
Put the jelly in the fridge	as it's your birthday.
I know it's time to get up	because my alarm clock is ringing.
You can go first	before it's too late!

DEFINITION
clause: A group of words that contains a verb and a noun or pronoun.

DEFINITION
conjunction: A type of connective that joins clauses within a sentence.

Using a dictionary

Learning objective: to know how to use a dictionary

A dictionary is a reference book that lists words and their meanings in alphabetical order.

For example:

doctor comes before **engineer**
scientist comes before **teacher**

d comes before **e**, and **s** comes before **t** in the alphabet.

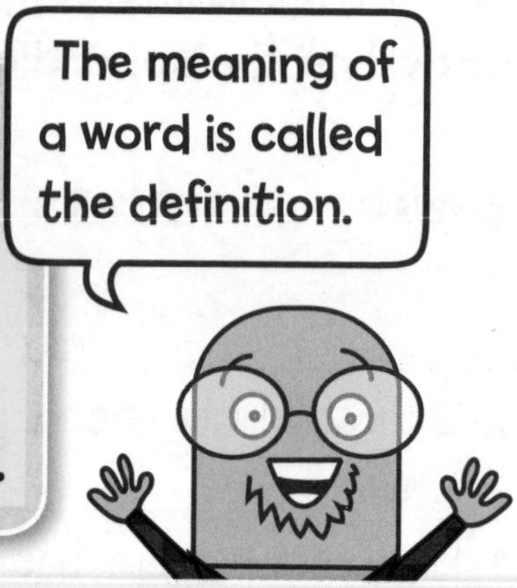

The meaning of a word is called the definition.

A

For each list of words, write 1st, 2nd, 3rd or 4th in the boxes, according to the order they would appear in a dictionary.

Nouns		Verbs	
lemur	☐	knit	☐
tarantula	☐	write	☐
ostrich	☐	print	☐
armadillo	☐	sew	☐

B

Draw lines to match the words to the correct definitions.

Word	Definition
dart	lean to one side
lurch	move uncomfortably
quake	move in circles
squirm	move quickly
twirl	shake with fright

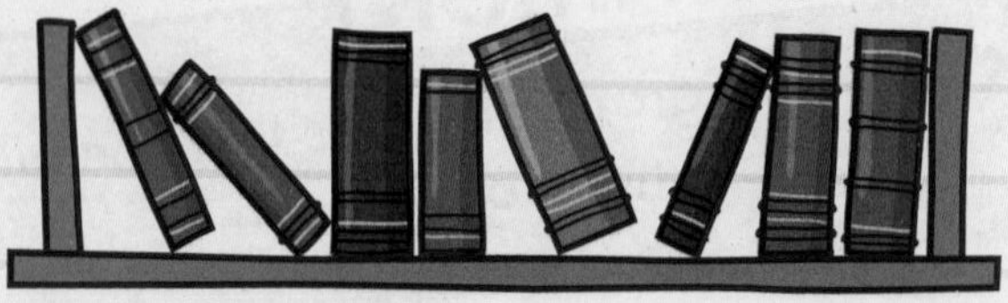

C

Read the words and the definitions. Write a sentence using each of the words defined.

1. **ideal**   something just right

_____

_____

2. **identical**   exactly the same

_____

_____

3. **imaginary**   not real

_____

_____

4. **immense**   very big

_____

_____

D

Rewrite these two lists of words in alphabetical order. You may need to look at the second, third or fourth letters to sort them!

1. agree
   apple
   attach
   angle
   afraid
   asleep
   absent

2. quiz
   quiet
   quarter
   quell
   quack
   quest
   quick

Fiction and non-fiction

Learning objective: to distinguish between fiction and non-fiction

Fiction books contain made-up stories. Non-fiction books contain information and fact. Fiction and non-fiction books are written in different ways.

Fiction books usually have:
- dialogue
- characters
- a story or plot
- illustrations

Non-fiction books usually have:
- information and facts
- photographs
- diagrams or maps
- an index

A

Label these book titles as either F for fiction or NF for non-fiction. Write in the box next to each one.

1. How Volcanoes Work ☐
2. Primary Science ☐
3. Bedtime Stories ☐
4. Teddy Goes to Toytown ☐
5. A History of the Vikings ☐
6. Treasure Island ☐

DEFINITION

dialogue: Conversation and words that are spoken.

index: An alphabetical list of things in a book, with the page numbers on which each one appears, to make it easy to find things. Look at the index on page 190 of this book.

My book is called *Morris and the Aliens*. Do you think it is fiction or non-fiction?

Sort your books at home into fiction and non-fiction collections.

B

Read the texts A, B and C extracted from different books and match them to the correct book titles below:

Disappearing Worlds

Wizardy Woo

Secrets and Spies

A. It was on the night of the next full moon that things began to go wrong. Spells that had worked perfectly well for hundreds of years had suddenly lost their magic....

From title: _____

B. Supergirl sped past the secret agents in her souped-up spy car. She had to reach Point Blank before they did. Her secret life depended on it!

From title: _____

C. The world's rainforests are vitally important to us. But every hour, thousands of square kilometres of trees are being cut down all over the world.

From title: _____

C

Which of these books would be in the fiction section and which in the non-fiction section of a library? Write the titles in the correct columns.

Fiction   Non-fiction

Fiction comprehension

Learning objective: to understand fiction text

Read the passage below and answer the questions about it.

Sale starts today

Anxious faces peer in through the shop window.

Inside, the manager's forehead wrinkles as she frowns. The 'SALE!' sign on the rack keeps falling off. Her fingers fumble as she hurriedly tapes the sign back in place.

As the crowd gathers outside, like sharks around a carcass, the shop assistants stare out anxiously. They dread the store opening.

The manager smoothes out the creases in her skirt and buttons her jacket. She takes a deep breath and walks towards the doors. With each step she feels like an underwater swimmer moving against the current.

Click! The key opens the lock and the doors bang open. The manager is pushed back, like a seashell carried on a wave, as people surge through the shop doors. The mayhem begins.

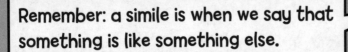

Remember: a simile is when we say that something is like something else.

A Write a sentence to answer each question.

1. What do you think the story is about?

2. Who is waiting outside the shop?

3. How do you think the manager is feeling?

4. What simile is used to describe the masses gathered outside?

5. Which two similes are used to describe the manager?

6. What mayhem is about to begin?

7. Write an alternative title for the story.

Fables

A fable is a short story with a moral lesson. The characters in fables are often animals.

A In Aesop's fable of 'The Dog and His Bone' below, some words have been left out. Predict what the words might be and write them in the spaces.

A dog was hurrying home with a big bone _____ the butcher had given him. He growled at everyone _____ passed, worried that they might try to steal it _____ him. He planned to bury the bone in the _____ and eat it later.

As he crossed a bridge _____ a stream, the dog happened to look down into _____ water. There he saw another dog with a much _____ bone. He didn't realise he was looking at his _____ reflection! He growled at the other dog and it _____ back.

The greedy dog wanted that bone too, and _____ snapped at the dog in the water. But then _____ own big bone fell into the stream with a _____ , and quickly sank out of sight. Then he realised _____ foolish he had been.

Who was Aesop?

Aesop was probably a Greek storyteller who lived over 2000 years ago.

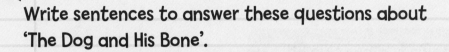

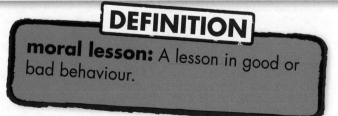

Research some other Aesop's fables at your local library.

B

Write sentences to answer these questions about 'The Dog and His Bone'.

1. Why was the dog hurrying home?

2. Why did the other dog growl back?

3. What lesson do you think the dog learned?

4. What is the moral of the fable? Tick the correct answer: a, b or c.
   a) Waste not want not.
   b) It is foolish to be greedy.
   c) Be happy with how you look.

5. If you rewrote the fable using the same moral but a different animal character, which animal would you choose? Say why.

DEFINITION

moral lesson: A lesson in good or bad behaviour.

95

Alliteration

Learning objective: to recognise alliteration

Alliteration is when we put together words that start with the same sound.

For example: This monster movie is a massive hit.

Write each idea on a new line.

A

Write a list poem, using alliteration.

One wiggly worm.

Two _____ _____

Three _____ _____

Four _____ _____

Five _____ _____

Six _____ _____

Seven _____ _____

Eight _____ _____

Nine _____ _____

Ten _____ _____

I'm jumping for joy! Is that an alliteration?

B

Complete the magazine headlines below using alliteration. Choose words from this list.

DOGS   LONG   TWOSOME   LOCKS   TERRIBLE   RECYCLE   DRAMA

REUSE AND _____

DANCING _____ IN SCHOOL _____

TWINS ARE A _____ _____

LOOK AFTER YOUR _____ _____

C

Complete these sentences using fun alliterations.

My alligator	is called Albert	and he's adorable.
My bear	is called Baloo	and he's big.
My c_____	is called C_____	and he's c_____ .
My d_____	is called D_____	and she's d_____ .
My e_____	is called E_____	and she's e_____ .
My f_____	is called F_____	and she's f_____ .

DEFINITION

alliteration: Words that begin with the same sounds.

Classic poetry

Read this extract from 'The Pied Piper of Hamelin' by Robert Browning.

Rats!
They fought the dogs, and killed the cats,
And bit the babies in the cradles,
And ate the cheeses out of the vats,
And licked the soup from the cook's own ladles,
Split open the kegs of salted sprats,
Made nests inside men's Sunday hats,
And even spoiled the women's chats,
By drowning their speaking
With shrieking and squeaking
In fifty different sharps and flats.

A

Now answer the questions.

1. What is the extract about?

2. Look at the first two lines. Which words are alliterations - that is, begin with the same sounds?

3. Find five words in the poem that rhyme with **cats**.

> ## DEFINITION
>
> **classic:** A classic is a great book or piece of writing usually from long ago.

Robert Browning was a famous writer who lived from 1812 to 1889.

4. What is a **ladle**?

5. How many cooks are there? What does the apostrophe in **cook's** tell us?

6. Why do you think the poet chose these three words: **speaking**, **shrieking** and **squeaking**?

7. What are **Sunday hats**?

8. Which two lines of the poem show that the rats make a tuneless and annoying noise?

9. If you've heard the story of the Pied Piper of Hamelin, write down what you know about it. If you're not familiar with the story, try to find a library copy.

DEFINITION

cradle: A small cot that swings.
sprat: A small fish.

Nonsense poems and limericks

Learning objective: to understand different types of poems

Read this nonsense poem and answer the questions below.

The Vulture
The Vulture eats between his meals
And that's the reason why
He very, very rarely feels
As well as you and I.

His eye is dull, his head is bald,
His neck is growing thinner.
Oh! what a lesson for us all
To only eat at dinner!

Hilaire Belloc

A

1. Which two words in the poem are on the ends of their lines, but do not actually rhyme?'

2. Why did the poet choose the word **thinner**?

3. What lesson does the poem teach us?

4. Do you think this is a serious poem? Explain your answer.

Read the limerick out loud.
Which lines rhyme with which?

Read the limerick below and answer the questions.

There was a young lady of Twickenham
Whose boots were too tight to walk quickenham.
She bore them awhile,
But at last, at a stile,
She pulled them both off and was sickenham.

Anon

DEFINITION

nonsense poem: A poem that doesn't make sense.
limerick: A five-line comic poem with a rhyme pattern.
anon: Anonymous. It means that we don't know who wrote the poem because it was written a long time ago.

B

1. Why has the poet made up the words **quickenham** and **sickenham**?

2. What does **she bore them awhile** mean?

3. Write down a limerick that you know or make up one of your own.

Playscripts

Learning objective: to understand how to read a playscript

Read the playscript below.

Scene 1: A New Puppy
Two dogs talking in the park.
Characters:
  Buster: Bulldog
  Sindy: Yorkshire Terrier

BUSTER: (wailing) A new puppy! After everything I've done for them.

SINDY: I knew you'd be upset. I told Mindy when I heard.

BUSTER: I take them for lovely walks, I eat up all their leftovers – even that takeaway muck they always dish out on a Friday… and this is the thanks I get!

SINDY: (sympathetically) You can choose your friends but you can't choose your owners.

BUSTER: What can they want a puppy for anyway?

SINDY: Well, puppies are cute.

BUSTER: Cute! Aren't I cute enough for them?

SINDY: Er…

BUSTER: Well, I'm telling you now. It's not getting its paws on my toys. I've buried them all!

How to write a playscript:
• Write the speaker's name then what they say.
• Start a new line for each speaker.

How to write a prose story:
• Start a new paragraph for each speaker.
• Put speech marks around the words spoken and include the speaker's name in the sentence.

A

Now rewrite the playscript as a prose story. Fill in the missing words.

Chapter 1: A New Puppy

"_____!" Buster wailed. "_____
_____."

"I knew you'd be upset," replied Sindy. "_____."

"I take them for lovely walks, I eat up all their leftovers – even that takeaway muck they always dish out on a Friday _____
_____!" said Buster.

"You can choose your friends but you can't choose your owners,"
_____.

"_____?" cried Buster.

"Well, puppies are cute," said Sindy.

"_____?" replied Buster.

"Er..." said Sindy.

"Well, I'm telling you now," said Buster. "_____
_____!"

Formal letters

Learning objective: to read and understand a formal letter

Read these formal letters and write a sentence to answer each question.

6 Acorn Avenue,
Newbridge,
N16 5BH

Monday, 7 May 2017

Dear Miss Smith,

I would be grateful if you would allow Becky to leave school early tomorrow afternoon. She has an appointment at the dentist at 3.15 pm but I need to pick her up from school at 2.45 pm. I'm sorry that she will miss the last lesson of the day but this was the only time available.

As Tuesday is homework night, perhaps I could take Becky's homework with me when I come to collect her.

Yours sincerely,

Mrs Alice Kenwood

A

1. If Becky's appointment is at 3.15 pm why does she need to leave at 2.45 pm?

2. On what day of the week is Becky's appointment?

3. Why does Mrs Kenwood apologise for taking Becky early?

4. Becky thinks she won't have to do her homework. Is this true?

Mrs A Kenwood,
6 Acorn Avenue,
Newbridge,
N16 5BH

Monday, 7 May 2017

Botchit Kitchens,
Dead End Lane,
Newbridge,
NO1 1NR

Dear Sir,

I am writing to complain about your company's shoddy workmanship on my recently fitted new kitchen.

Firstly, all of the doors are hanging off their hinges. Secondly, the drawers have been fitted upside-down so we can't put anything in them. Thirdly, you forgot to make room for the sink! What use is a kitchen without a sink?

I want to know when you are able to put these things right. Please call me to arrange a time as soon as possible.

Yours faithfully,

Mrs A Kenwood

B

1. Whose address is printed on the left-hand side of the page?

2. What does 'shoddy' mean in the first sentence?

3. What is the purpose of the letter?

4. From reading the letter, how do you think Mrs Kenwood is feeling?

Instructions

Learning objective: to understand instruction text

Read the instructions and then answer the questions below.

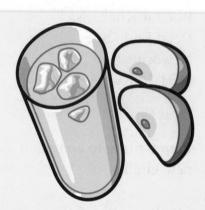

Apple and Raspberry Refresher

Ingredients (serves 1):
4 ice cubes
1 tablespoon raspberry syrup
250 ml apple juice
thin slices of apple for decoration

What you do:
1. Put the ice cubes in a plastic bag and crush them with a rolling pin.
2. Tip the ice into a glass.
3. Pour on the raspberry syrup.
4. Fill the glass to the top with apple juice.
5. Decorate with thin slices of apple.

A

1. What other things will you need in addition to the list of ingredients?

2. Is there enough for two glasses?

3. Do you need apple slices to make this drink?

4. The instructions include the following words: put, tip, pour, fill, decorate. Are these words nouns, verbs or adjectives?

5. Write an alternative name for this drink.

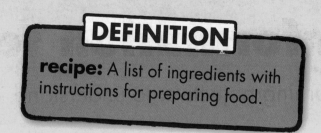

DEFINITION

recipe: A list of ingredients with instructions for preparing food.

Look at the recipe and read the instructions.
Can you spot any missing ingredients?

Chicken Salad Supreme Sandwich

Ingredients:
bread
margarine
cooked chicken
lettuce leaves
tomatoes

What you do:
1. Butter the bread.
2. Put the chicken on the bread.
3. Spread on some mayonnaise.
4. Add tomatoes and lettuce.
5. Then sandwich together.

This recipe is badly written because:
• The list of ingredients is incomplete.
• We don't know how much we need of anything.
• Some steps are missing from **What you do**.

B

Rewrite the recipe in your own words. Try to make big improvements on the original.

Information text

Read this page carefully, then write a sentence to answer each question about it on the opposite page.

The Spanish Armada

In 1587, Elizabeth I was Queen of England and Philip II was King of Spain. The two leaders disagreed over religion. When Elizabeth signed a death warrant for the Catholic Mary Queen of Scots to be executed, it was the final straw for Philip. He ordered an invasion.

In 1588, Philip sent an Armada of 130 warships to invade England. But the English saw them coming and set sail, meeting the Spanish Armada in the English Channel. The Spanish ships sailed in a crescent shape around the English fleet. The English knew they would have to break this formation to defeat the Armada.

So the English sent burning ships to sail into the Spanish Armada. The plan worked and the Armada scattered. The Spanish ships were large, heavy and slow to move and turn. The English ships were smaller and could turn quickly. They had better cannons too, which caused a lot of damage to the Spanish ships.

The Armada tried to escape back to Spain by sailing north but bad weather blew the ships towards the coasts of Ireland and Scotland. Many ships were wrecked against the rocks.

Only half of the ships that set out in the Armada made it back to Spain. None of the English ships was lost. It was one of Elizabeth's greatest victories.

Information text is found in non-fiction books.

A

1. Why do you think Philip was angry when Mary Queen of Scots was executed?

2. What does 'it was the final straw for Philip' mean?

3. Why would a crescent shape of Spanish ships be a problem for the English?

4. How did the English plan to break up the Armada?

5. What advantages did the English ships have?

6. Where was the Armada shipwrecked?

7. Approximately how many Spanish ships survived the battle?

8. How many English ships survived?

Shape and acrostic poems

Read the shape poem.

Egg

Yellow yolk
for my breakfast,
with dip-in soldiers.
I love eggy bread,
boiled, fried, scrambled,
or poached eggs... How do
you like your eggs?
"Made from chocolate,
of course!"

How to write a **shape poem**:
- Draw an outline of a familiar object.
- Write your poem inside the outline, following the shape.
- Don't worry about rhyme - it doesn't have to rhyme.
- Try to include alliteration, e.g. yellow yolk.

A This circle shape could represent a ball, a bubble, the Sun or the Moon - you decide. Then write a shape poem of your own inside the circle.

This is an acrostic poem. The first letter in each line spells a name.

My brother
Always kicking a ball or
Running recklessly
CRASH! Into me!
OUCH! Look where you're going!

Here's another example:

   P L A Y F U L
     C U **T** E
  Y E L **P**
      P A W
F U R R **Y**

How to write an **acrostic poem:**
- Write about something or someone that you know well.
- Spell out the subject of your poem vertically down the page.
- Alongside each letter continue with a descriptive phrase or word.

B

Write an acrostic poem of your own in the space below.

Settings

Learning objective: to write a description of a known setting

A setting is the place where the events in a story happen.

A

The story below is set in a girl's bedroom. Read the story, then answer each question below.

> Everything matched: walls, bed, cushions, carpet, dolls – everything was either purple or pink.
>
> Her princess bed was fluffed up with pretty pink pillows and purple sequins sparkled all around.
>
> Rose-scented perfume filled the air and a bubbling, purple lava lamp gave off a soft, warm, purplish glow.
>
> But on the day a friend gave her a strange-looking orange ring, her cosy, pink world would change forever!

1. What sort of a person would have a bedroom like this?

2. Circle any alliterations that you spot in the second paragraph.
3. What do you think she thought when her friend gave her an orange ring?

4. Do you think the ring is going to be important in the story? Say why.

Say this tongue twister:
Princess was pretty in pink!

Find a description of a setting in a fiction book.

Writers often set their stories in places that they know well, e.g. places they've visited, school or work. But sometimes writers use historical settings or imaginary places.

B

Think about a place that you know well. For example, it could be your bedroom, classroom or friend's room.

Write words that describe what you...
see:
hear:
feel:
smell:
taste:

Now use your notes to write a short description.

How to write a description of a place:
- Picture the place in your mind.
- Imagine the sounds, smells and feel of the place.
- Write down your ideas in a clear order.
- Use adjectives to describe it.

Characters

Learning objective: to write a character description

Read the character descriptions and answer the questions below.

1. Grandpa Bob, old and gnarled, like an ancient oak, sits rooted in his armchair, surrounded by his books. Age has not dulled his sense of humour or his mind, which is still as sharp and clear as ever.

2. Auntie Deera was round and plump with a soft, sunny face. When she laughed, which was often, her tummy laughed too. Her favourite saying was, "You'll never guess what happened to me today…"

3. Zak was a terrible two-year-old and a tearaway at ten. Every day at primary school, his cheeky grin got him into and out of mischief. "It wasn't me!" he'd say.

4. Charlie's blue eyes are outlined with thick, black mascara. A skull tattoo on her arm makes her look hard, but I know she's not.

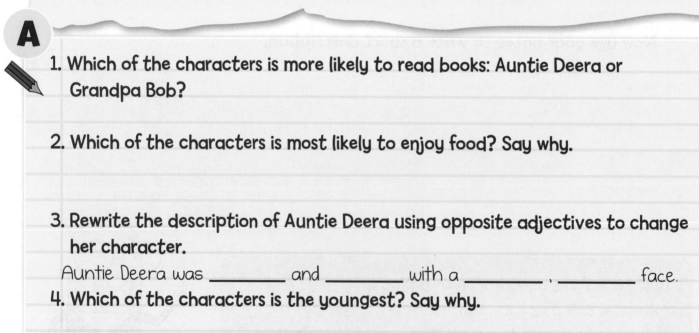

A

1. Which of the characters is more likely to read books: Auntie Deera or Grandpa Bob?

2. Which of the characters is most likely to enjoy food? Say why.

3. Rewrite the description of Auntie Deera using opposite adjectives to change her character.
   Auntie Deera was _____ and _____ with a _____ , _____ face.

4. Which of the characters is the youngest? Say why.

5. How old do you think Charlie is?

Try writing a description of me! What adjectives would you use?

B

Write descriptions for each of these characters. Describe their personalities and behaviour, as well as what they look like.

Miss Harshly, teacher

Bulky Bazza, weightlifter

A.T., alien being

Write a character description of someone that you know well.
Disguise their true identity by changing their name, as many writers do!

How to write a character description:
• Choose names carefully that suggest a character, e.g. Mrs Jolly.
• Ask yourself questions, e.g. What's their personality? What do they like to do?
• Different characters should speak differently, e.g. they might have favourite sayings.
• Give your character an unusual feature, e.g. eyes of different colours.

Story plans and plots

Learning objective: to learn how to plan a story

Now it's time to write your own story. Try these story-planning tips.

1. Choose a book you have enjoyed and imitate it, changing the setting, the characters and the events.

> For example: you could write a story based on 'The Three Billy Goats Gruff' but change the troll to a bully and the Billy Goats Gruff to you and your friends!
>
> I was walking home from school with Gaz and Tim when we saw him, swinging on the gate.

2. Retell something that has happened to you but change the characters and the setting.

> For example: write a story based on something you lost. Perhaps it belonged to someone else!
>
> Where could it have gone? I'm in big trouble now. Mum doesn't even know I had it!

3. Use more than one theme, e.g. good and evil, friendship, lost and found, a long journey, rags to riches.

> For example: write a story that explores two themes - friendship and rags to riches.
>
> Cindy carried her empty suitcase to the station. She pretended it was heavy so that the others wouldn't know she had nothing to put in it.

The characters should be changed by the events in your story. For example, an evil character might see the error of his or her ways and become a good person.

Don't try to write your story without first making a plan. Your plan might be a spider diagram, a storyboard or a written list. Look at these plans for a retelling of 'The Three Billy Goats Gruff'.

The Troll and the Three Billy Goats (retold)

Storyboard

Billy goats teasing troll	Troll lonely	Small billy goat falls
Troll saves him	Making friends	Troll is happy

List

1. Billy Goats tease Troll.
2. Troll is lonely.
3. Smallest Billy Goat falls off the bridge.
4. Troll saves him.
5. Billy Goats make friends with Troll.
6. Now Troll is happy.

Spider diagram

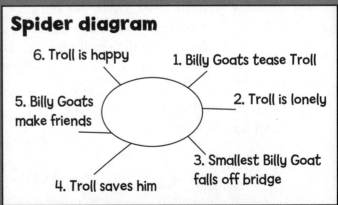

6. Troll is happy

5. Billy Goats make friends

4. Troll saves him

1. Billy Goats tease Troll

2. Troll is lonely

3. Smallest Billy Goat falls off bridge

Now try planning and writing your own story on a separate piece of paper.

117

Biography

Learning objective: to understand how to write a biography

A book or a piece of writing that is an account of a person's life is called a biography.

A

The paragraphs below are all from the biography of Roald Dahl. But they are mixed up. Read them carefully and then write the order you think they go in.

Biography of Roald Dahl (1916–1990)

1. After school, he worked for the Shell Petroleum Company in Tanzania and in 1939, at the start of the Second World War, he joined the Royal Air Force.

2. He recovered and resumed duties in 1941 but then he started to suffer from headaches and blackouts.

3. Sadly, when he was just four, his seven-year-old sister died from appendicitis and a month later his father died from pneumonia.

4. He began writing in 1942 after being sent home from the army. His most popular children's books include *Charlie and the Chocolate Factory*, *James and the Giant Peach* and *The BFG*.

5. In 1940, Dahl was out on a mission when he was forced to make an emergency landing. Unluckily he hit a boulder and his plane crashed, fracturing his skull and his nose and temporarily blinding him.

6. Dahl married in 1953 and had five children.

7. Roald Dahl was born in Cardiff in 1916, the son of Norwegian parents.

I think that the paragraphs should go in the following order:

DEFINITION

timeline: A line representing a period of time on which dates and events are marked.

B

Write a biography of a friend or relative. Use this space to plan a timeline of their life, writing key events above the line and dates below it.

Born

Now write the biography in this space.

Persuasive writing

Learning objective: to learn to write persuasively

Read the snippets of text taken from an advertising leaflet for Awesome Towers.

AWESOME TOWERS!

- Have you got what it takes to ride the biggest rollercoaster?
- Special holiday season tickets
- Park and ride
- Gift shop
- New this year!

AWESOME TOWERS!

- A fabulous day out for all the family!
- There's something for everyone...
- Fantastic fun-packed activities for all ages.
- Ride awesome rollercoasters.
- Watch spectacular live shows.
- Enjoy an excellent choice of cafés and restaurants.
- You're guaranteed to have fun!

Next time you visit an attraction pick up a leaflet and notice how it is written.

A

Now write a leaflet advertising a major attraction near you.

Amazing day out! Come rain or shine!

Holiday discount prices

Buy one ticket, get one free!

How to write persuasive text:
- Use adjectives, e.g. biggest, best, terrific, exciting, guaranteed, great.
- Use verbs, e.g. enjoy, see, find, discover, watch, ride, go, eat.
- Speak to the reader, e.g. use the pronoun 'you'.

Writing a review

Learning objective: to write a review of a book, song or film

Read the book review below. Notice how it is set out under different headings.

<u>Title</u>: Kensuke's Kingdom
<u>Author</u>: Michael Morpurgo

<u>Brief outline of the story</u>
The story is about a boy called Michael and his family who set off to sail around the world. One stormy night, Michael and his dog get washed overboard. They are rescued by Kensuke, an old man who lives on a desert island.

<u>Strengths</u>
I liked the way the author wrote about the friendship between Michael and Kensuke. It seemed very real, like a true story.

<u>Weaknesses</u>
I think it was sad at the end when Michael left the island. I usually prefer stories with happier endings. But if Michael had stayed, his parents would have been unhappy.

<u>Recommendation</u>
This is a wonderful book. Children over 8 years old would enjoy it, as I have.

<u>Score</u>
9/10

DEFINITION

review: An opinion or criticism of something.

Write a list of your top three books, songs and films.

Write a review of a book, song or film that you have enjoyed.

Title:

Author/artist:

Brief outline of the story/song

Strengths

Weaknesses

Recommendation

Score

        /10

How to write a review:
• Give details about the book/song/film.
• Write about the things you liked.
• Write about the things you didn't like.
• Give a recommendation: say who would enjoy it.

Teeth

You have two sets of teeth during your lifetime:

· Milk teeth grow when you are teething as a baby and begin to drop out when you are about seven.

· Permanent teeth replace milk teeth and have to last all your life.

Types of teeth

Teeth break up food into small pieces so that you can swallow it. There are three types of teeth.

incisor Chisel-shaped teeth for cutting up soft food such as fruit.

canine Pointed teeth for tearing tougher food such as meat.

molar Teeth with lumpy tops for grinding and mashing up the food into tiny pieces.

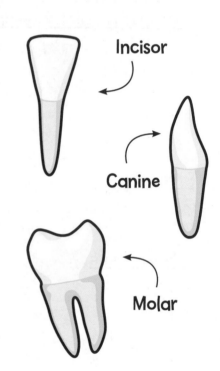

Incisor

Canine

Molar

A

Match the tooth with its purpose by drawing a line between them.

Tooth	Purpose
canine	cutting
molar	tearing
incisor	grinding

Can you find the three different types of teeth in your mouth?

The care of teeth

Learning objective: to know how to keep teeth healthy

A sticky coating called plaque covers your teeth. Microbes settle in the plaque and feed on sugar in your food. They make acid which rots your teeth. Cleaning your teeth brushes off the plaque so the microbes have nowhere to live. Toothpaste stops the acid working.

- Clean the back of your teeth as well as the front.
- Don't eat or drink anything after you have cleaned your teeth at night because the microbes will start feeding again.

Eat hard foods such as celery, raw carrots or crunchy apples as snacks, to help keep your teeth clean.

DEFINITION

microbes: Tiny forms of life that can only be seen with a microscope.
acid: A substance that can break up other substances.

B

Choose the correct words to fill in the spaces below.

Microbes   healthy   clean   coating   teeth   acid   plaque

Plaque is a sticky _____ that covers the teeth. _____ live in it and make _____ that rots your _____ . When you _____ your teeth you remove the acid and _____ and keep your teeth _____ .

Food groups

All our foods can be sorted into four food groups.

Protein
Meat, fish, eggs, beans, lentils, nuts

Fruit and vegetables
Apples, oranges, pears, mangoes, potatoes, carrots, cabbage, onions, peas

Carbohydrates
Rice, pasta, bread

DEFINITION

carbohydrate: Plants make this substance which is sometimes called starch.

Fats and sugars
Butter, cheese, sweets, biscuits

Which group is your favourite food in?

A

Write the name of each food in this meal and its correct group.

Food	Group
apple	fruit and vegetables

126

How the body uses food

Learning objective: to link food groups to their uses in the body

The foods in each group help the body in a special way.

Healthy eating

This food pyramid will help you remember how much of each type of food to eat to stay healthy. Eat small amounts of foods from the top of the pyramid and larger amounts of the foods lower down.

Fats and sugars give the body energy.

Protein helps the body grow and repair.

Carbohydrates give the body energy for action.

Fruit and vegetables keep the body healthy and working well.

B

 Draw a line between each food and the way it helps the body.

Gives you energy

Keeps you healthy

Helps you grow

Do you eat healthily like the pyramid suggests?

The parts of a plant

Learning objective: to know and recognise the parts of a plant

There are four main parts to a plant.

The flower
A plant may have one or more flowers. The large brightly coloured parts are called petals.

The leaf
Most leaves are green but some may have white or coloured parts.

The stem
The stems of many plants are green and bendy.

The root
Roots are pale and spread out through the soil.

The stem of a tree is made of wood and covered in bark. It is called the trunk.

What the plant parts do

Learning objective: to learn the purpose of each part of the plant

Each plant part has an important job to do.

The flower
The flower makes pollen. Pollen is carried away by insects or the wind. The flower also receives pollen from other flowers of the same kind that it needs to make seeds.

The leaf
The leaf makes food. Food is made from the sunlight and air around the leaf together with water and minerals from the roots.

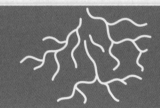

The stem
The stem holds up the leaves and flowers. It also carries water and food from the roots to all parts of the plant.

The roots
The roots hold the plant in the ground. They also take in water and minerals from the soil.

A

1. Write labels on the plant opposite pointing to the correct parts:

   root   stem   leaf   flower

2. Move your finger over the picture opposite to show how water moves through the plant.

DEFINITION

minerals: Substances in the soil that the plant takes in to stay healthy.

129

Plant growth

Learning objective: to know experiments can be made to investigate plant growth

You can test the effects of leaves, light, water and warmth on plant growth by making fair tests.

How to measure growth
Measure the length of the stem to show how much the plant grows.

Experiment 1: Testing leaves
Two plants were given the same amount of water, light and warmth. One plant had new leaves carefully cut off whenever they grew.

Experiment 2: Testing light
One plant was put in a cupboard and one plant was kept near a sunny window. The picture shows how the plants looked after two weeks.

A

1. In experiment 1, which plant grew better after two weeks: A or B? How were the two plants different?

2. In experiment 2, which plant grew better after two weeks: A or B? How were the two plants different?

3. In experiment 2, why do you think plant B has grown so tall?

130

DEFINITION

a fair test: A test in which all the conditions except one are kept the same.

Have a go at the experiments on this page yourself.

Experiment 3: Testing water

Five pots of cress seedlings were watered each day. The table shows how much water each pot was given. After two weeks the plants were examined and their stems were measured.

Pot	Amount of water per day (cm³)	Stem length (cm)
A	5	0 (dead)
B	10	3.5
C	15	7
D	20	3
E	25	0 (dead)

Experiment 4: Testing warmth

Two pots of cress seedlings were set up. One pot was covered with a transparent plastic cup to make a mini greenhouse. The picture shows how the pots looked after a week.

B

1. What do the results of experiment 3 show?

2. What is the effect of warmth on plant growth?

A greenhouse traps the Sun's heat to make a warm place for plants.

Types of rock

Learning objective: to learn about the three types of rock

There are three types of rock. They form in different ways.

Igneous rocks

Rocks formed deep in the Earth where it is very hot:
Basalt is black.
Granite can be many colours.

Metamorphic rocks

Rocks formed from other rocks that have slipped inside the Earth and been heated up:
Slate is grey and made from mud layers stuck together in thin sheets.
Some marble is made from crystals like sugar.

Sedimentary rocks

Rocks formed from small particles stuck together:
Sandstone is yellow and made from grains of sand.
Limestone is grey and made from seashells.
Chalk is white and made from very tiny seashells.

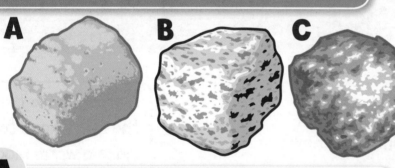

D **E**

A **B** **C**

F **G**

A

Read the descriptions and look at the pictures. Write down the letter of each rock next to its name.

Basalt		Limestone		Marble	
Granite		Chalk			
Sandstone		Slate			

Can you find any of these rocks around your home?

132

The properties of rocks

Learning objective: to learn how the properties of rocks can be tested

Rocks can be tested for hardness and the way they react with water.

Hardness test

Rub together two rocks over white card.
The rock that crumbles most is soft.
The rock that crumbles least is hard.

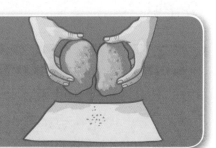

Water test

Test the rocks by pouring on a spoonful of water.
If the rock is porous, the water disappears into it.
If the rock is non-porous, the water remains on the top.

B

1. Look at the table and fill in the last column.

Rock	Water on rock	Porous/non-porous
Granite	Stays on top	
Limestone	Sinks into rock	
Sandstone	Sinks into rock	
Basalt	Stays on top	

DEFINITION

porous: Having tiny spaces in it called pores.

2. Slate has been used to make the roofs of houses. Do you think it is porous or non-porous? Why?

Soil

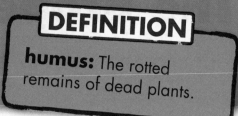

DEFINITION

humus: The rotted remains of dead plants.

Soil is made from a mixture of rock particles and humus. Soils vary from place to place.

Comparing the parts of a soil sample

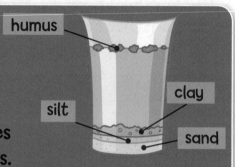

- Put some soil in a jar to about a fifth of the way up.
- Pour in water almost to the top.
- Stir the mixture for about a minute.
- Let it settle. The humus floats and the rocky particles sink. The particles at the bottom separate into layers.

humus

clay

silt

sand

Sieving soil

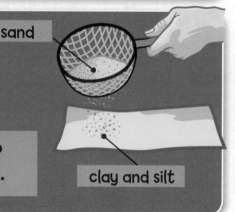

Use a sieve to separate soil particles of different sizes. The larger particles stay in the sieve and the smaller particles fall through the holes.

For example, clay and silt particles are small enough to pass through this sieve but sand particles are trapped.

sand

clay and silt

A

1. Circle the particles that settle first.

    clay   sand   silt

Stir up some potting compost and water, then let it settle to compare its parts.

2. Circle the particles that settle last.

    clay   sand   silt

3. What do you need to separate silt from clay?

    A. a sieve with holes large enough for both types of particles

    B. a sieve with holes large enough for one type of particle

The drainage of soil

Learning objective: to learn how drainage is compared in a fair test

Spaces between soil particles let water through. If the spaces are large, the water passes through the soil quickly and the soil drains well. If the spaces are small, the water passes slowly and the soil drains poorly.

Comparing the drainage of soils
- Put the same amount of each soil in a funnel lined with filter paper.
- Pour the same amount of water on each soil sample.
- After five minutes, measure how much water has passed through.

B

$100cm^3$ of water was added to three soil samples and the water was collected and measured after five minutes. This table shows the results.

Soil sample	Water added (cm^3)	Water drained (cm^3)	Water still in the soil (cm^3)
A	100	60	
B	100	43	
C	100	71	

1. How much water was left in the soil after five minutes? Fill in the table above.
2. Circle which soil has the best drainage:
   A B C

3. Circle which soil has the worst drainage:
   A B C

Magnets and materials

Magnetic force is stronger near each end of a magnet. These are called the poles of a magnet. A magnet floating on a cork will line up its poles with the Earth's North and South Poles.

When two magnets meet

When the poles of two magnets are brought together they may join together because the forces attract each other or they may spring apart because the forces repel each other.

Look at what happens when two magnets are brought together in three different ways:

A

B

C

A

1. What is happening in picture A?

2. What is happening in picture B?

3. What is happening in picture C?

4. What do opposite (unlike) poles do? Circle the answer.

   attract   repel

5. What do similar (like) poles do? Circle the answer.

   attract   repel

136

Can you make fridge magnets attract and repel each other?

Testing materials

• You can test materials by bringing a magnet close to them. Objects made of iron and steel are magnetic materials so they will stick to a magnet.

• Objects made of pottery, wood, cloth and plastic are non-magnetic so they won't stick.

A magnet and cardboard

If you put a magnet on top of a piece of cardboard, then put a paperclip underneath, the paperclip will stick to the cardboard. The force of the magnet acts through the cardboard. If you move the magnet, the paperclip on the other side moves too.

Testing the strength of magnets

To test the strength of a magnet, attach one paperclip after another to make a chain. The strongest magnet will have the longest chain. Another way to test magnetic strength is to place more and more sheets of card between a magnetic pole and a paperclip until the paperclip falls off.

B

1. In the paperclip test above which magnet is the strongest?

2. Which is the weakest?

Springs

Learning objective: to learn that springs generate forces

There are two types of common springs: a close-coiled spring where the coils touch each other and an open-coiled spring where the coils do not touch.

Close-coiled springs and forces

If you stretch a close-coiled spring, a tension force forms in the spring. You can feel it pulling on your fingers. This force pulls the spring back to its original length when you let go of one end. You cannot squash a close-coiled spring because the coils are already touching.

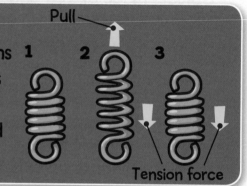

Pull

1   2   3

Tension force

Open-coiled springs and forces

When you squash an open-coiled spring a compression force forms in the spring. You can feel it pushing on your fingers. This force pushes the spring back to its original length when you let go of one end. You can also stretch an open-coiled spring just as you can a close-coiled spring.

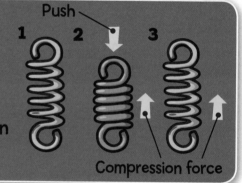

Push

1   2   3

Compression force

A

1. What will happen if a weight is put on top of spring A and then spring B?

2. What will happen if a weight is hung from spring A and then spring B?

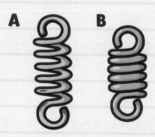

A   B

Elastic bands

Learning objective: to learn that elastic bands generate forces when stretched

Stretch an elastic band by pulling in one direction and the elastic pulls back in the other direction. That's why, when you stop pulling, the band snaps back to its original shape.

A push meter
An elastic band can be used to make a push meter.

- Stretch the elastic band between two nails.
- Draw a scale on one side to measure the pushing force.
- Push a toy car into the elastic band and measure its position on the scale.
- Then let the car go so that it shoots away.
- Now measure the distance it has travelled.

Ask an adult to help you make your own push meter!

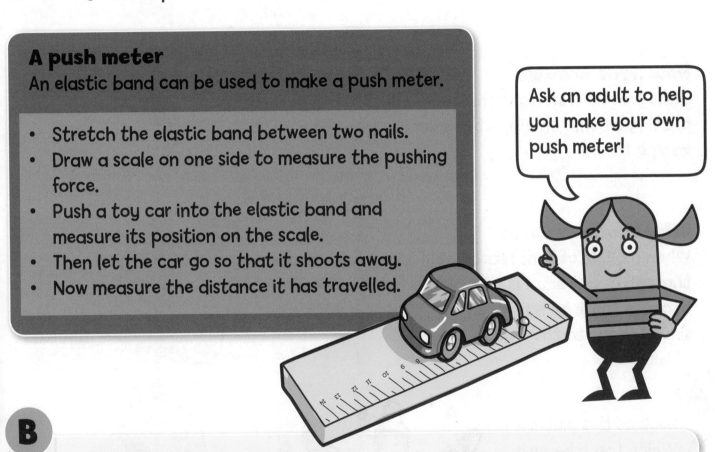

B

When a toy car is pushed back along the scale to 4 it shoots away 20 centimetres. How far do you think it would go if:

1. It was pushed along the scale to 1? Circle the correct answer.

about 1cm   about 5cm   about 30cm

2. It was pushed along the scale to 6? Circle the correct answer.

about 1cm   about 5cm   about 30cm

Light and shadows

Light travels from its source in straight lines. When light reaches most objects it is stopped from travelling and a shadow forms behind the object.

How light travels
Light travels in straight lines. You can test this by putting a comb on a sheet of paper in front of a shining torch.

Why shadows form
When a beam of light hits an object but cannot pass through it, a shadow is cast on the far side. It is black because the light is blocked. The shadow will have a similar shape to the object.

A

Look at this picture. Which torch beam is casting the shadow?

A   B   C

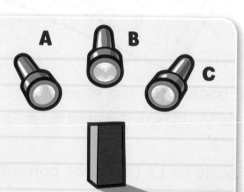

DEFINITION

light source: Something that gives out light, such as the Sun, an electric lamp or a candle flame.

Materials and light

Learning objective: to learn about opaque, transparent and translucent materials

Light cannot pass through most materials but it does pass through some.

Opaque materials stop light rays passing through them.
You cannot see through them.
They cast dark shadows.

Transparent materials let most of the light rays pass straight through them.
You can see clearly through them.
They cast pale shadows.

Translucent materials let some of the light rays through them but scatter them.
You cannot see clearly through them.
They make quite dark shadows.

B

Put an O in the boxes of materials that are opaque.
Put a TP next to materials that are transparent.
Put a TL next to materials that are translucent.

clear plastic ☐   frosted glass ☐   greaseproof paper ☐

window glass ☐   brick ☐   orange juice ☐

wood ☐   cardboard ☐

water ☐   metal ☐

DEFINITION

light ray: A very thin, straight beam of light.

The Sun and shadows

Learning objective: to know that as the Sun moves shadows change

The morning Sun rises in the east. It climbs in an arc through the sky until it reaches its highest point at midday. In the evening, it sets in the west. As the Sun moves, the shadows cast by objects change.

When the Sun is rising in the east, long shadows are cast towards the west.

When the Sun is at its highest, at midday, short shadows are cast pointing north.

When the Sun is sinking in the west, long shadows are cast towards the east.

Remember, never look directly at the Sun. It can damage your eyes.

A

A    **B** 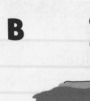   **C**

What time do you think it is at A? Circle the correct answer.

06.30   13.00   18.30

What time do you think it is at B? Circle the correct answer.

09.00   12.00   14.00

What time do you think it is at C? Circle the correct answer.

06.00   10.00   14.30

142

How shadows change

Learning objective: to link the height of a light source with shadow length

Try this experiment, using a torch as the Sun and a block for a tree.

Investigating shadow length
- Shine the torch onto the block from different heights. Keep the torch at the same angle.
- For each height of the torch, measure the length of the shadow.

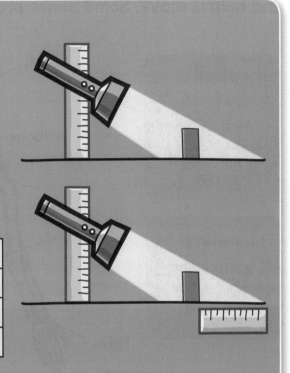

Here are some results already recorded:

Height of torch (cm)	Length of shadow (cm)
5	55
10	35
15	25

B

Write T (true) or F (false) next to each statement.

A As the torch rises the shadow gets longer. ☐

B As the torch rises the shadow gets shorter. ☐

C As the torch sinks the shadow gets longer. ☐

Try this experiment with your own torch.

The human skeleton

The human skeleton has 206 bones. They work together to support the body and help it move. Some bones protect organs in the body.

The **skull** is made from a group of bones that protect the brain.

The **pelvis** attaches the leg bones to the spine.

The **shoulder blade** and **collarbone** attach the arm bones to the spine.

The **ribs** form a cage which protects the heart and lungs and moves to help us breathe.

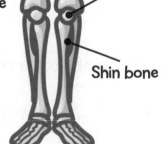

Skull

Collarbone

Shoulder blade

Spine

Breast bone

Pelvis

Rib

Thigh bone

Kneecap

Shin bone

DEFINITION

organ: A body part which performs a particular task. For example, the heart is an organ which pumps blood around the body.

Can you find and feel the bones labelled on the diagram on your own body?

 A

✎ Draw arrows to show which bones link.

thigh bone	spine
arm bone	pelvis
rib cage	collarbone

Animal skeletons

Learning objective: to learn that animals have different types of skeletons

Many animals have bony skeletons but some have skeletons made of shell, a horn-like material or even water.

Bony skeletons

Fish, amphibians, reptiles (scaly-skinned animals), birds and mammals (animals with hair) have bony skeletons with a skull and a spine. Fish have bones that support their fins, and reptiles such as snakes do not have arm or leg bones.

Animals with a skeleton of armour

Some animals have a skeleton made from hard material on the outside of their bodies. Crabs and shrimps have a skeleton made of shell. Insects and spiders have a skeleton made from a substance with properties similar to horn and finger nails.

Animals with a water skeleton

Earthworms and slugs have spaces in their bodies that are full of water. These spaces act like a water skeleton and support the body.

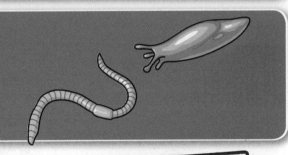

B

Match the animal with its skeleton by drawing lines between them.

slug
frog   skeleton of bone
shrimp   skeleton of armour
spider   water skeleton
snake

DEFINITION

amphibian: An animal with a smooth skin, which has a tadpole stage in its life, e.g. a frog.

145

Movement

Learning objective: to learn how muscles move bones

Muscles are attached to bones to make the body move. A muscle can contract itself, but it can't stretch itself. Muscles often work in pairs.

Pairs of muscles

The biceps and the triceps work together in the upper arm to make the lower arm move.

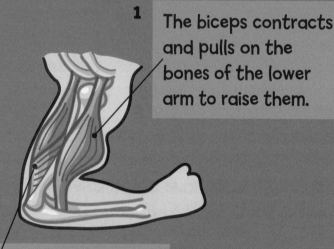

1 The biceps contracts and pulls on the bones of the lower arm to raise them.

The triceps is stretched by the contracting biceps.

2 The triceps contracts and pulls on the bones of the lower arm to lower them.

The biceps is stretched by the contracting triceps.

Stretch out your right arm. Spread out the fingers of your left hand and press them into your biceps. Bend your right arm. What do you feel with your fingers?

DEFINITION

contract: To make shorter.

146

Exercise

Learning objective: to learn that exercise helps to keep the body healthy

Exercise keeps bones, joints and muscles strong.

Keep an exercise diary for a week. Write down what you did and how long you did it.

A

Choose the correct words to complete the sentences below.

fat	stored
food	pumps
oxygen	energy

Did you do more exercise or less exercise than you thought? Do you need to do more?

The heart
The heart is a muscle that _____ blood around the body. Blood takes _____ and oxygen to all parts of the body. When the muscles exercise, they need more food and _____ so the heart pumps faster.

Exercise and fat
Energy from food is _____ in the body as fat. Too much ____ makes the body heavy and puts a strain on muscles and the heart. Exercise uses up _____ and stops the body getting overweight.

DEFINITION

joints: The places where bones are joined together such as at the elbow or the knee.

The size of habitats

Learning objective: to know that organisms live in habitats

The place where an organism lives is called its habitat. There are different sizes of habitat.

Micro habitat
This is the smallest type of habitat. Underneath a stone where a centipede lives or the underside of a leaf, which is home to greenfly, are micro habitats.

Mini habitat
This is made up from many micro habitats. A bush has micro habitats which include the bark where beetles live, leaves where caterpillars feed, flowers where spiders hide to catch insects and roots where eelworms gather to feed.

Habitat
This is the largest habitat. It is made up from micro and mini habitats. A forest is a habitat that is made up from trees, bushes, grass and ground covered with stones and dead leaves.

 A

 **A**    **B**    **C**   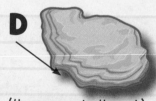 **D**

(the space under the rock)

Identify the habitats in A–D by circling the correct answer.

A   habitat   mini habitat   micro habitat
B   habitat   mini habitat   micro habitat
C   habitat   mini habitat   micro habitat
D   habitat   mini habitat   micro habitat

DEFINITION

organism: A living thing such as a plant or an animal.

148

The conditions in a habitat

Learning objective: to know that organisms in a habitat are adapted to its conditions

Each habitat has a set of conditions which organisms adapt to in order to survive there.

B

Choose the correct words to complete the sentences below.

ferns	shady	mosses
salt	limpets	waterlilies
fish	wet	crabs

The forest habitat
Trees make the forest _____. Plants such as _____ and _____ can grow here. They are adapted to growing in dim light.

The pond habitat
A freshwater pond is cool and ___. Organisms such as _____ and ___ can survive here. They are adapted to living in fresh water.

The rocky shore habitat
A rocky shore is partly covered by _____ water. Organisms such as _____ and _____ can survive here. They are adapted to the salty waves.

The crab breathes in salty water. It hides when the tide comes in.

The limpet has a sucker to grip the rock. Its shell stops it losing water when the tide is out.

Swellings, called bladders, help seaweed fronds to float so that it can stay in the light to make food. A holdfast, like a root, grips the rock so that the seaweed is not swept away by the waves.

Grouping living things

Learning objective: to use the features of organisms to put them into groups

Every organism has some features which it shares with other organisms. We group together organisms with shared features to make it easier to study them.

Here are some major groups of animals and their features:

Animal group	Features
Insects	Six legs
Spiders	Eight legs
Fish	Scales and fins
Amphibians	Smooth slimy skin
Reptiles	Scaly skin
Birds	Feathers
Mammals	Hair or fur

You could also check out the definition of amphibian on page 145.

A

1. Write the letter of each animal next to the group it belongs to.

Animal group	Animal
Insects	
Spiders	
Fish	
Amphibians	
Reptiles	
Birds	
Mammals	

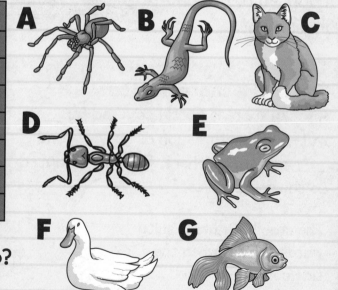

A B C

D E

F G

2. Which animal group do humans belong to?

150

Keys

Learning objective: to learn how to use a key to identify organisms

A key is a set of questions about the features of a group of organisms.
Each answer helps to identify the organism.

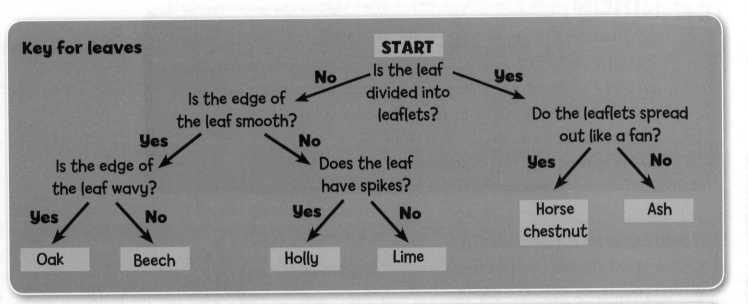

Key for leaves

START

Is the leaf divided into leaflets?

No → Is the edge of the leaf smooth?

Yes → Do the leaflets spread out like a fan?

Is the edge of the leaf smooth?
- **Yes** → Is the edge of the leaf wavy?
- **No** → Does the leaf have spikes?

Is the edge of the leaf wavy?
- **Yes** → Oak
- **No** → Beech

Does the leaf have spikes?
- **Yes** → Holly
- **No** → Lime

Do the leaflets spread out like a fan?
- **Yes** → Horse chestnut
- **No** → Ash

Look at leaf **F** below. Is it divided into leaflets? Is the edge of the leaf smooth? Does it have spikes? You should have got to the answer lime.

B Use the key to identify the leaves.

A

B

A

B

C

D

E

F

A

B

C

D

E

F

Food chains

Learning objective: to understand food chains

Some organisms in a habitat make food and others eat it.

DEFINITION

producers: Organisms that make food. Plants are producers.
consumers: Organisms that eat food. Animals are consumers.
prey: An animal that is consumed by another animal.
predator: An animal that consumes another animal.
herbivores: Animals that eat plants.
carnivores: Animals that eat meat.

Organisms in a food chain

1. The plant makes food from air, sunlight and water.
2. The herbivore eats the plant.
3. The carnivore eats the herbivore.

Food chains can have more than three organisms in them. For example, if an eagle ate the fox it could be added to the food chain. The fox would be both predator and prey.

A

1. Draw a food chain with a human acting as a herbivore.

2. Draw a food chain with a human acting as a carnivore.

Note that the arrow always goes from the food to the feeder.

Protecting habitats

Learning objective: to understand the significance of
protecting habitats

Plants and animals are adapted to their habitat. If the conditions of the habitat change, the organisms may die or move away.

When a forest is cut down
- When trees are cut down, organisms lose their mini habitats.
- Predators, such as woodpeckers that feed on insects in the bark, do not have anything to eat and move away.
- Plants, such as ferns and mosses, are less adapted to direct sunlight and may not survive.

When a pond is drained
- Fish will die because they cannot move away.
- Frogs may hop away to find a new pond.
- Birds, such as herons, which feed on fish and frogs, move away to find food.
- Water plants cannot survive in dry soil and die.
- Birds that nested among the water plants move away.

Find out why the Earth's rainforests need protecting and make a poster about it.

B

Imagine that there are plans to drain a pond or clear forest near your home.

Write a letter to protest about the plan and encourage people to conserve the habitats.

DEFINITION

habitat: The place where an animal or plant lives.

153

Temperatures

Learning objective: to learn how to use a thermometer and record temperatures

A thermometer measures temperature. Temperature is measured in degrees Celsius, written as °C.

The parts of a thermometer

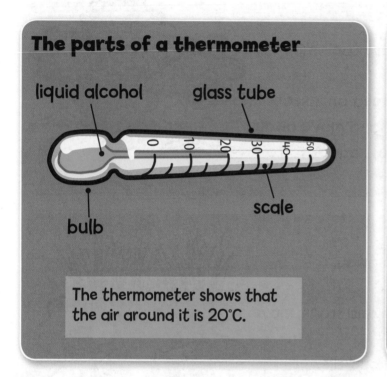

liquid alcohol   glass tube

scale

bulb

The thermometer shows that the air around it is 20°C.

Taking the temperature

• Leave the thermometer bulb in the liquid for a few moments.
• Read the liquid against the scale.

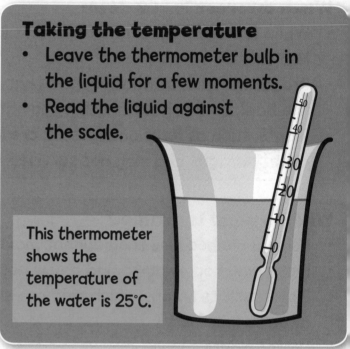

This thermometer shows the temperature of the water is 25°C.

A

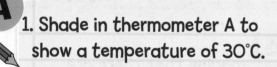

1. Shade in thermometer A to show a temperature of 30°C.

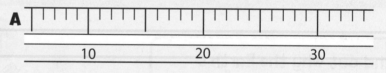

2. Shade in thermometer B to show a temperature of 25°C.

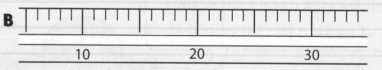

3. Shade in thermometer C to show a temperature of 33°C.

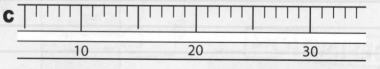

4. Shade in thermometer D to show a temperature of 39°C.

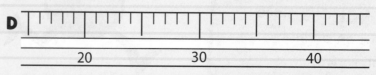

DEFINITION

temperature: A measure of the coldness or heat of something.

Temperature can change over time. These changes can be measured using a thermometer and a clock.

Recording temperature change
- Warm water was left to stand for four minutes.
- The temperature of the water was taken at the beginning and after every minute interval.

B

1. Fill in this table from the data in the pictures.

Time from start (minutes)	Temperature (°C)

2. Why were the last two temperatures the same?

3. Make a line graph from the data in the table.

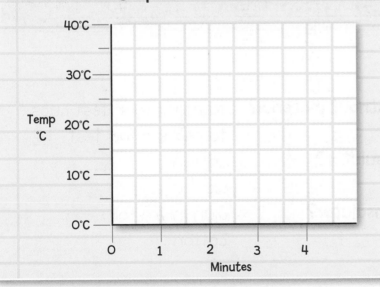

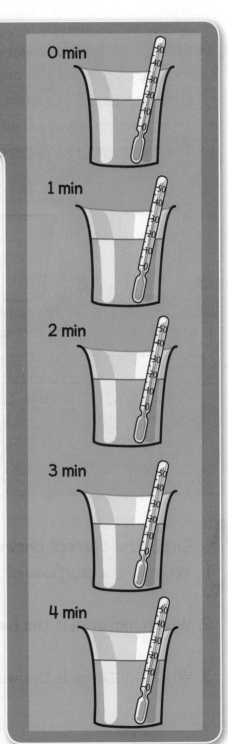

0 min

1 min

2 min

3 min

4 min

Heat insulators

Learning objective: to compare how materials prevent heat moving using a fair test

Heat moves from a warmer place to a cooler place. A material which greatly slows down the movement of heat is called a heat insulator.

Testing for heat insulation

- Plastic cups and lids are covered with materials.
- One cup and lid are left uncovered.
- The same amount of warm water is poured into each cup.
- The temperature is taken straight away and ten minutes later.

A   Wool   B   Aluminium foil   C   Cotton   D

The table shows how much the temperature changed:

Time (mins)	Cup A Temp (°C)	Cup B Temp (°C)	Cup C Temp (°C)	Cup D Temp (°C)
0	50	50	50	50
10	30	45	32	40

A Circle the correct answers.

1. What is the purpose of the cup without material?
   - to make four test cups
   - to make a fair test

2. Which material is the best heat insulator?
   - cotton
   - wool

3. Which material is the worst heat insulator?
   - aluminium foil
   - cotton

Heat conductors

Learning objective: to compare how quickly materials move heat using a fair test

A heat conductor is a material which heat moves through quickly. Materials can be tested to see if they are good heat conductors using butter, because butter melts when it is hot.

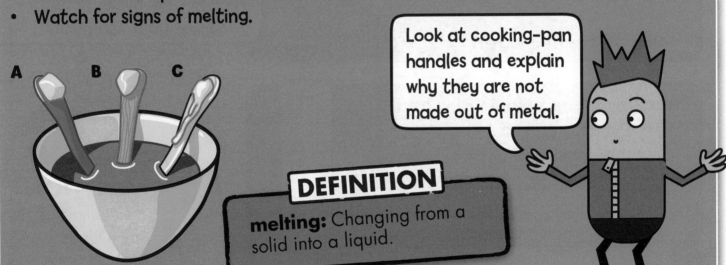

Testing for heat conduction
A lump of butter melts fastest on a spoon made out of the best heat conductor.
- Put a plastic, wooden and steel spoon of the same size in a bowl of hot water.
- Add a small lump of butter to each handle.
- Watch for signs of melting.

Look at cooking-pan handles and explain why they are not made out of metal.

DEFINITION

melting: Changing from a solid into a liquid.

B

1. Which spoon is made from the best heat conductor, A, B or C?

2. If you made a spoon out of aluminium foil and used it in this experiment, what do you think would happen?

3. How does the metal in cooking pans help food in the pans to cook?

Solids and liquids

Learning objective: to compare solids and liquids and measure their volumes

The shape of solids and liquids

A solid has a fixed shape. Its shape does not change if you turn it over or leave it for a long time.

A liquid has no shape. It fills the shape of any container it is poured into.

The volume of solids

Find the volume of a solid block:

*   Measure its height, width and length.
*   Multiply them together.

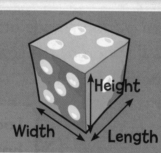

Height
Width
Length

Find a block of wood and find its volume. Then look at another block of wood, estimate its volume then measure it. How good was your estimate?

Measuring the volume of a liquid

Find the volume of a liquid:

*   Pour the liquid into a measuring cylinder on a flat, horizontal surface.
*   Bring your eye level with the liquid surface to read the scale.

DEFINITION

volume: The amount of space taken up by a substance. Volume is measured in cubic centimetres (cm³).

 A

1. What is the volume of liquid in each measuring cylinder?

Volume in A: _____ cm³

Volume in B: _____ cm³

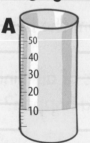
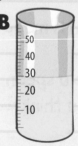

2. If the liquid from A is poured into B what will the volume of liquid in B measure?

Flowing

Learning objective: to compare runniness in liquids and powdered solids

Different liquids flow with different speeds. Their speeds can be compared in a runniness test. Tiny solid particles can also flow like liquids.

Comparing runniness
Test the runniness of liquids by letting them flow down a tube tipped at an angle. Time how long they take to reach the bottom.

Can you make salt or flour flow like a liquid?

Grains and powders
Small particles of solids, such as sand and salt, form grains. Even smaller particles of solids, such as pepper and flour, form powders. Grains or powder particles slide over each other easily. This makes them flow and they can be poured like a liquid. They are not a real liquid because they cannot form drops.

B

1. How is the runniness test made fair?

2. Can you fill in the results for the runniness test below by matching each liquid to the time it took to flow?

Pour water very slowly from a jug and look for drops. What happens when you pour flour slowly?

A

vegetable oil

B

treacle

C

water

Liquid	Time to flow (seconds)
	8
	20
	6

Melting

Learning objective: to know that when solids are heated up enough they turn liquid

If any solid is heated up enough it melts and becomes a liquid.

Melting

A solid keeps its shape at normal temperatures. If it is heated, it flows and becomes runny. When this happens it has melted – it has changed from a solid into a liquid. Melting is a reversible change.

For example, a candle is made from wax which melts when it gets hot and turns into a liquid.

A

Here are the melting points of four substances:

Substance	Melting point (°C)
A	200
B	750
C	430
D	850

DEFINITION

reversible change: A change that can be reversed because it has an opposite. The opposite of melting is freezing.

melting point: The temperature at which a solid melts is called its melting point.

1. The four substances are heated up in a furnace. Put them in the order in which they melted.

2. Circle the substances that are still solid at 500°C.
   A   B   C   D

3. When A melts, how much hotter must the furnace get before D melts?
   550°C   650°C   230°C

160

Freezing

Learning objective: to know that when liquids are cooled down enough they freeze

If any liquid is cooled down enough it freezes and becomes a solid.

Freezing

A liquid flows at normal temperatures. If it is cooled, it becomes solid. When this happens it has frozen. Freezing is a reversible change.

For example, to make an ice lolly you freeze liquid water in a container. It becomes a solid and takes on the fixed shape of the container.

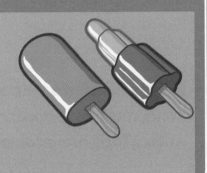

Freezing point

The temperature at which a liquid freezes is called its freezing point. This is the same as the melting point of the solid that it forms.

For example:
- The freezing point of water is 0°C.
- The melting point of ice is 0°C.

Different substances freeze at different temperatures. They do not all freeze at 0°C. The molten wax drippng down a candle becomes solid when its temperature drops to 50°C.

What is the opposite of freezing?

B

Choose the correct words to fill in the spaces in the sentences below.

| hot | solid | side | liquid | 600°C | flowing | freezing | away |

The molten rock _____ down the _____ of a volcano is a _____ and may be as _____ as 1200°C. It cools as it moves _____ and when it reaches _____ it stops flowing and becomes _____ rock. The _____ point of the rock is 600°C.

161

Dissolving

Learning objective: to know that some solids dissolve in water and others do not

When some solids are stirred in water they fall to the bottom, forming a layer. They do not dissolve. But other solids disappear into the water when they are stirred. These solids dissolve in the water.

Solids that do not dissolve
Sand, marble, chalk and glass beads do not dissolve in water. They are insoluble.

Solids that dissolve
Sugar and salt dissolve in water by splitting into tiny particles. They are soluble.

Coloured solid, coloured solution
Some solids, such as instant coffee granules, are coloured. When they dissolve they colour the water too.

DEFINITION

solution: The mixture of tiny solid particles dissolved in liquid. The particles can only be seen under a microscope.

A

1. Which of these substances dissolve in water? Tick the boxes.

chalk ☐   sugar ☐   instant coffee granules ☐
salt ☐   marble ☐   sand ☐

2. Loose tea leaves turn hot water brown, but they also form a layer at the bottom of the cup or teapot. Explain what is happening.

Filtering

Learning objective: to understand how filtering can be used to separate materials

A filter is a material with holes in it which lets a liquid pass through.

Filtering sand and water mixture
- Pour water mixed with sand into a filter paper.
- The sand grains cannot pass through because they are too big.
- The water passes through the filter.
- The sand and water are separated by filtering.

Filtering salt water solution
- Pour salt dissolved in water into a filter paper.
- The salt particles pass through with the water because they are so tiny.
- The salt in the solution cannot be separated by filtering.

B

1. **What happens when you filter a chalk and water mixture?**
   a. The chalk stays in the filter paper and the water passes through.
   b. The water stays in the filter paper and the chalk passes through.
   c. The chalk and water both pass through the filter paper.

2. **What happens when you filter a sugar and water solution?**
   a. The sugar stays in the filter paper and the water passes through.
   b. The water stays in the filter paper and the sugar passes through.
   c. The sugar and water both pass through the filter paper.

3. **Is the paper in a tea bag a filter? Explain your answer.**

The force meter

Learning objective: to learn how to use a force meter

A force meter is used to measure the strength of pulling forces. It is also called a newton meter because force is measure in newtons.

The parts of a force meter

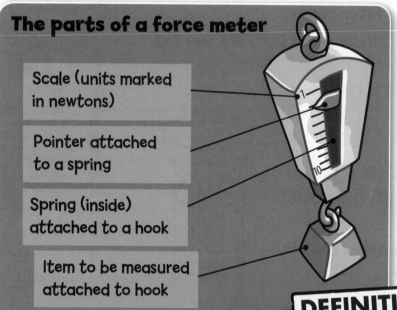

Scale (units marked in newtons)

Pointer attached to a spring

Spring (inside) attached to a hook

Item to be measured attached to hook

How to measure the force of a weight

1. A weight is attached to the hook.
2. The hook pulls on the spring.
3. The spring is stretched, moving the pointer.
4. A reading is taken from the scale where the pointer stops.

DEFINITION

newton: The unit in which forces are measured. One newton (N) is about equal to the weight of an average sized apple.

A

What size of force does each of these force meters read?

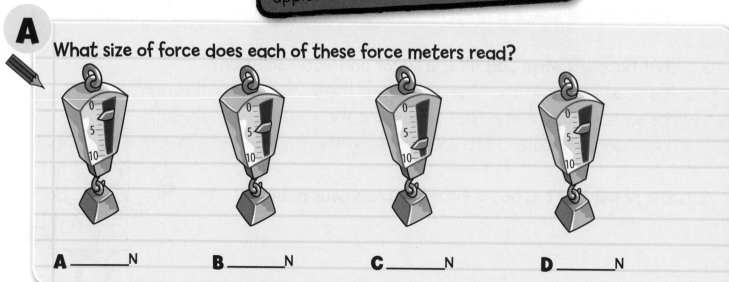

A _____ N   B _____ N   C _____ N   D _____ N

Friction

Learning objective: to learn about friction

Push your foot along a floor and you can feel the force of friction.

Friction is a force made when two surfaces are pushed or pulled against each other. Friction acts in the opposite direction from the pull or push. If the push or pull is weak, the force of friction will match it in strength and the surfaces will not slide. When the push or pull reaches a certain strength, it overcomes the force of friction and the surfaces move.

Push → ← Friction

A force meter and friction
A force meter can be used to find the force needed to overcome the force of friction.

A slope and friction
When a wooden block is placed on a tray and one end raised slightly, gravity pulls on the block and friction holds the block in place. At some point, as the end is raised, gravity overcomes friction and the block slides. The height of the slope at which the block starts to slide is used to measure the force of friction.

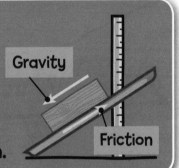

Gravity

Friction

B

When the slope method was used to test the friction between a block and different materials on the slope, the following readings were made:

Make a slope like the one above, put different shoes on it and tip it up. Which shoe has the best grip?

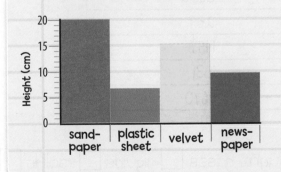

Arrange the materials in the order of the strength of friction between them and the block, strongest first.

1.

2.

3.

4.

Vibration

Learning objective: to learn that sounds are made by vibrations

A sound is made when something vibrates. A vibration is a to-and-fro or an up-and-down movement. Vibrations can move through different materials.

Making vibrations

- If a ruler is held firmly over the edge of a table and 'twanged', it vibrates up and down and makes a sound.
- An elastic band stretched between finger and thumb vibrates to and fro when it is plucked. It also makes a sound.

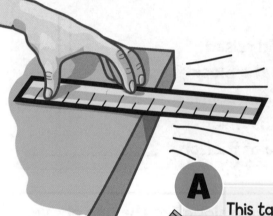

A

Try twanging a ruler over the edge of a table.

Travelling sound

- When an object vibrates in air, the air around it starts to vibrate.
- This makes air further away vibrate.
- The vibration passes through the air as a wave – a sound wave.

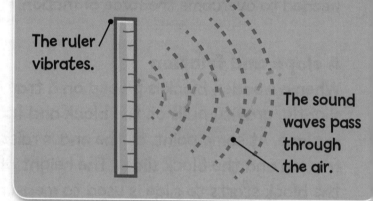

The ruler vibrates.

The sound waves pass through the air.

This table shows the speed of sound waves through some materials.

Material	Speed (m per second)
Air	343
Brick	3650
Carbon dioxide	259
Fresh water	1497
Sea water	1531
Wood	4670

Tick the correct box:

Sound travels fastest through... gases ☐ liquids ☐ solids ☐

Sound travels slowest through... gases ☐ liquids ☐ solids ☐

Loud and soft

Learning objective: to understand about loud and soft sounds

Large vibrations make loud sounds and small vibrations make quiet sounds. Vibrations may be absorbed into some materials so that little or no sound is heard. These materials are called sound insulators.

Measuring loudness

The decibel (dB) is the unit used to measure the loudness of sounds. Here are some examples of quiet and loud sounds.

Sound	Loudness (dB)
Road drill	110
Vacuum cleaner	80
Busy street	70
People talking	50
Quiet street	40
Whisper	30
Pin drop	10

Guess how loud it is around you now using the decibel scale. Try it at other times too.

Sound insulation

Try testing materials to see how well they insulate sound.

- Wrap the material around a sound source, such as a radio.
- Measure the distance at which the source sound can no longer be heard.

B

1. How do you think a sound insulation test could be made fair?

2. A radio could not be heard 2 metres away when wrapped in material A and could not be heard 50 centimetres away when wrapped in material B. Which material was the better sound insulator?

Electrical components

Electrical components are the items that make up an electrical circuit. NEVER use mains electricity for experiments.

Battery

Electricity from the battery powers the circuit. It is sometimes called a cell. The power of the battery is measured in volts (V). Batteries for science circuits should be 1.5V.

positive terminal

battery power in **volts**

negative terminal

Switch

This controls the flow of electricity around a circuit.

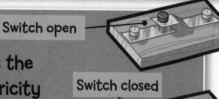

Switch open

Switch closed

Wires

Metal wires coated in plastic conduct electricity around the circuit.

Motor

Electricity flows through the motor driving the motor shaft round.

motor shaft

Buzzer

The buzzer makes a sound when electricity flows through it.

Lamp

filament

The lamp lights up when electricity flows through it. The part that lights up is called the filament.

A Draw a line to match each component with what it is used for:

motor	conducts electricity
wire	controls the flow of electricity
buzzer	provides movement
switch	makes a sound

DEFINITION

circuit: A loop made by joining electrical components together so that a current of electricity can flow through them.

Making a circuit

Learning objective: to recognise when a circuit will conduct electricity

A circuit is made by connecting up the components and passing an electric current through it.

Making connections

Connections are important in a circuit because if there is a gap anywhere in the circuit, the electric current cannot flow.

- The switch acts as a gap in the electric circuit.
- When the switch is closed, the current flows.
- When the switch is open, the current does not flow.

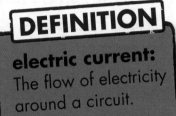

DEFINITION

electric current:
The flow of electricity around a circuit.

Electricity cannot flow through circuit B because the switch is open so there is a gap in the circuit.

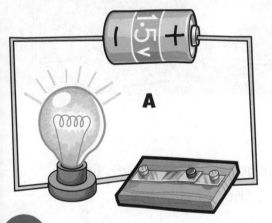

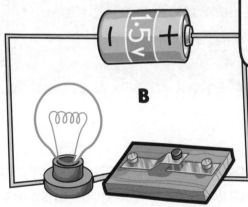

B

Could electricity flow through this circuit?
Explain your answer.

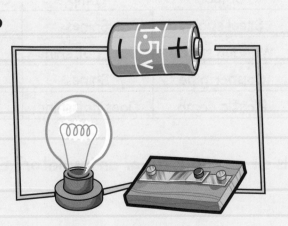

Testing for flow

Learning objective: to test materials to find out if they conduct electricity

Materials which let electricity flow through them are called electrical conductors.

Materials which do not let electricity flow through them are called electrical insulators.

Testing materials

- Place the materials in a gap left in the circuit.
- Press the switch on.
- If the lamp lights up, electricity is flowing through the material. This means that the material is a conductor.
- If the lamp does not light up, electricity is not flowing through the material. This means the material is an insulator.

Place material to be tested here.

A

1. Which objects are made from materials that are conductors and which from materials that are insulators? Write your answers in the third column.

Object	Lamp	Conductor or Insulator
Steel spoon	Shines	
Wooden spoon	Does not shine	
Copper pipe	Shines	
Plastic comb	Does not shine	

2. Is air a conductor or an insulator? Explain your answer.

Switches

Learning objective: to make switches from simple materials

A switch has two metal contacts.
- When the switch is off, the metal contacts do not touch and the air between them acts as an insulator so a current of electricity does not flow.
- When the switch is on, the contacts touch and electricity flows round the circuit.

If you have a torch, see if you have to press or slide the switch to complete the circuit and turn the torch on.

Paperclip switch
To turn the switch on, move the paperclip so it is touching both drawing pins to complete the circuit.

Pressure switch
To turn this switch on, press the two inside surfaces together so that the two pieces of foil touch, completing the circuit. It makes a good burglar alarm hidden under a mat – it turns on if anyone steps on it.

B

Choose the correct words to explain how this switch works.

electricity   tipped   ball bearing   wires

When the tube is _____, the _____ rolls onto the ends of the _____ and _____ can flow through it from one wire to the next.

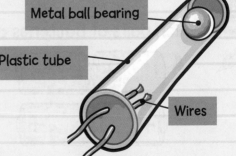

Metal ball bearing

Plastic tube

Wires

Using more batteries

Electricity flows from a negative terminal to a positive terminal.

Lining up batteries

- If two batteries are lined up in a circuit, a positive terminal has to connect with a negative terminal.
- If two batteries are lined up with the positive terminals connected or the negative terminals connected, the current will not flow.

Batteries and lamps

1. When two 1.5V batteries are included in a circuit, the power of the current rises to 3V (1.5V + 1.5V = 3V). This makes a lamp shine more brightly.
2. When three 1.5V battery are included in a circuit, the power of the current rises to 4.5V. If the voltage of the lamp is less than 4.5V the current will burn out the lamp.
3. If the voltage of a lamp is higher than 4.5V the lamp will shine more brightly.

 **1**

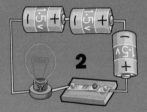 **2**

 **3**

 A

Which pairs of batteries allow electricity to flow? Tick the boxes.

A  ☐   B  ☐

C  ☐   D  ☐

172

Using more lamps

Learning objective: to learn how the arrangement of lamps affects their brightness

The wire filament in a lamp resists the flow of an electric current. This resistance makes the filament hot so the lamp lights up.

Lamps in a row

1. In a single lamp, the filament offers resistance to a current and lights up.
2. In a row of two lamps in series, the resistance of one filament adds to the resistance of the second and slows down the current. This means two lamps do not shine as brightly as a single lamp.

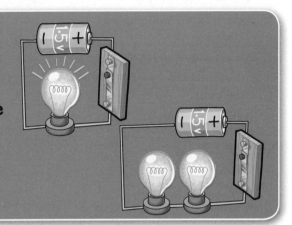

Lamps side by side

1. If two lamps are arranged side by side in parallel, and each one is connected separately to the battery and switch, the resistance of one filament does not add to the resistance of the other filament. Both lamps shine as if they were in the circuit on their own.

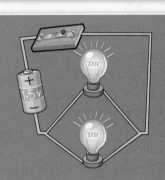

DEFINITION

resistance: The property of an electrical conductor that slows down the current of electricity passing through it.

Street lamps are arranged side by side in a circuit so if one goes out the rest stay lit.

B

Which arrangement below shines more dimly than the other two?

A

B

C

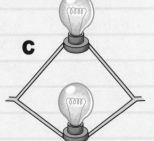

Answers

Pages 10–11

A 1. 300 + 90 + 8
2. 200 + 10 + 7
3. 3000 + 700 + 0 + 9

B 1. nine hundred and forty-one
2. 326
3. five hundred and thirty-four
4. two thousand, eight hundred and seventy
5. 1219
6. 2650

C 1. 83
2. 545
3. 911
4. 628
5. 2704
6. 7638

Pages 12–13

A 1. 147 is less than 152.
2. 476 is less than 479.
3. 753 is more than 735.
4. 521 is more than 381.
5. 190 is less than 390.
6. 1214 is less than 1244.
7. 5860 is more than 5850.
8. 5920 is more than 4970.

B 1. 264 > 254
2. 328 < 431
3. 190 > 119
4. 1536 > 1523
5. 2708 < 2807
6. 6550 > 6350

C 1. 112, 125, 159, 191
2. 278, 373, 387, 483
3. 622, 645, 668, 739
4. 1410, 1461, 2416, 2460
5. 2743, 2760, 3704, 3778
6. 3309, 3459, 4195, 4815

Pages 14–15

A 1. 70, 60
2. 0, -25
3. 125, 100
4. 320, 220
5. 450, 475
6. 350, 300
7. 1568, 1468
8. 5931, 6931

B 1. 85, 145 The rule is +15
2. 500, 450 The rule is -50
3. 943, 743 The rule is -100
4. 619, 419 The rule is -100
5. 820, 840 The rule is +5
6. 472, 502 The rule is +10
7. 113, 103 The rule is -10
8. 512, 527 The rule is +3

C 1. 995, 985, 975, 965, 955, 945, 935
2. 80, 180, 280, 380, 480, 580, 680
3. 857, 855, 853, 851, 849, 847, 845

Pages 16–17

A 1. 7 + 8 = 15   15 - 7 = 8
   8 + 7 = 15   15 - 8 = 7
2. 6 + 6 = 12   12 - 6 = 6
   6 + 6 = 12   12 - 6 = 6
3. 9 + 5 = 14   14 - 9 = 5
   5 + 9 = 14   14 - 5 = 9
4. 9 + 7 = 16   16 - 9 = 7
   7 + 9 = 16   16 - 7 = 9

B 1. 15, 150, 1500
2. 4, 40, 400
3. 12, 120, 1200
4. 2, 20, 200

C 1. 9
2. 8
3. 18
4. 4
5. 60
6. 900
7. 50
8. 200

D 1. 90
2. 14
3. 7
4. 600
5. 700
6. 40

Pages 18–19

A 1. 67
2. 57
3. 35
4. 29
5. 198
6. 178

B 1. 76
2. 78
3. 82
4. 43
5. 180
6. 190

C 55 + 20 → 72 + 3
62 + 6 → 48 + 20
171 + 8 → 129 + 50
137 + 30 → 163 + 4
84 + 5 → 49 + 40

D 1. 37
2. 42
3. 54
4. 64
5. 46
6. 84

Pages 20–21

A 1. 42
2. 84
3. 23
4. 128
5. 63
6. 12
7. 42
8. 162

B 1. 95
2. 52
3. 73
4. 242
5. 76
6. 59

C

1.
IN	56	78	27	49	15	64
OUT	52	74	23	45	11	60

2.
IN	165	191	142	177	159	183
OUT	135	161	112	147	129	153

Pages 22–23

A 1. 24
2. 21
3. 36
4. 45
5. 30
6. 56

B 1. 35, 42
2. 40, 48
3. 60, 54
4. 96, 88
5. 9, 18
6. 24, 48
7. 16, 32
8. 18, 36

C 1. 24
2. 27
3. 3
4. 2
5. 5
6. 3; she will have some left over

Pages 22-23 Continued

D

2 x 9 → 18 4 x 7 → 28

x   x   x   x

6 x 9 → 54 9 x 3 → 27

↓   ↓   ↓   ↓

12   81   36   21

Pages 24-25

A 1. 200 + 70 + 15 = 285

   2. 100 + 70 + 18 = 188

B 1. 180   2. 344

   3. 2296   4. 2261

C 1. 93   4. 171

   2. 83   5. 294

   3. 72   6. 1451

D 1. 90km   5. 160 pages

   2. 67 bottles   6. 174cm

   3. 61 chickens and ducks

   4. 185 items

Pages 26-27

A 1. 35   2. 27

   3. 26   4. 58

   5. 125   6. 3559

B 1. 20   4. 151

   2. 27   5. 1615

   3. 422   6. 2929

C

a) 2	7	b) 1	c) 3	9
2	d) 3	5	9	e) 4
f) 4	1	g) 3	h) 1	5
6	i) 4	7	8	j) 8

Pages 28-29

A 1. 56   2. 225

   3. 222   4. 174

B 1. 152   2. 184

   3. 685

C 1. 172   4. 184

   2. 141   5. 804

   3. 171   6. 640

D 1. 192 people   4. 144 eggs

   2. 95km   5. 168 hours

   3. 210 melons   6. 177 biscuits

Pages 30-31

A 1. 9 r 3   4. 8 r 2

   2. 6 r 1   5. 5 r 5

   3. 7 r 2   6. 6 r 4

B 1. 28   6. 3

   2. 9   7. 6

   3. 6   8. 8

   4. 8   9. 7

   5. 3   10. 32

C 1. 11 teams

   2. 3 pupils

   3. 17 teams   1 left over

       8 teams   3 left over

       7 teams   0 left over

       5 teams   5 left over

       5 teams   0 left over

Challenge: 61

Pages 32-33

A 1. 5   2. 3   3. 9

   4. 3   5. 7

B 12 red, 4 yellow, 8 blue,

   6 large, 3 long

C 1. 7, 14   5. 7, 49

   2. 10, 30   6. 4, 28

   3. 3, 15   7. 11, 22

   4. 2, 16   8. 5, 25

Challenge: 16

Pages 34-35

A 1. 6.3   6. $\frac{8}{10}$

   2. 0.9   7. $7\frac{2}{10}$

   3. 12.4   8. $16\frac{7}{10}$

   4. 18.5   9. $20\frac{6}{10}$

   5. 11.1   10. $4\frac{9}{10}$

B 1. 2   4. $\frac{2}{10}$

   2. 20   5. $\frac{2}{10}$

   3. $\frac{2}{10}$ 6. 2

C 7.5   8.1   8.7   9.7

   12.9   13.4   13.8   14.3

D 1. >   5. >

   2. <   6. >

   3. >   7. <

   4. <   8. <

Answers

Pages 36-37

A 1. quadrilateral,   2. octagon,
    3. hexagon,   4. pentagon,
    5. triangle,   6. hexagon

B 1. Hexagons - odd one out is
     a quadrilateral.
   2. Quadrilaterals - odd one out is a
     pentagon.
   3. Ovals - odd one out is a circle.

Pages 38-39

A Symmetrical: leaf, TV, ladder
   Not symmetrical: car, cup, sock

B Check each shape drawn is an exact
   reflection.

C 1. M   4. U
    2. B   5. 3
    3. X

Challenge: DECK, CODE, HOOD,
            WHAT, TOW, HIM

Pages 40-41

B Check estimated angles are within
   5 degrees of these:
   1. 150°   2. 110°   3. 90°   4. 45°   5. 30°
   6. 130°   7. 70°   8. 90°

C

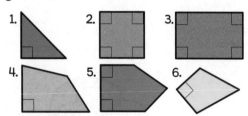

D The order should be:
   6 (30°), 4 (45°), 2 (60°),
   1 (100°), 3 (120°), 5 (160°)

Challenge: 32

Pages 42-43

A 1. cone   4. cuboid
    2. sphere   5. cylinder
    3. cube   6. prism

B 1. All cylinders. The odd one
     out is a cone.
   2. All cubes. The odd one
     out is a sphere.
   3. All cuboids. The odd one
     out is a prism.

C

Name of shape	cube	cuboid	prism
Total number of faces	6	6	5
Number of square and rectangle faces	6	6	3
Number of tri-angular faces	0	0	2

D 1. never   2. always
    3. never   4. sometimes

Pages 44-45

A Estimates should be within 1cm of the
   answers to section B.

B 1. 5cm   4. 7cm
    2. 8cm   5. 10cm
    3. 12cm   6. 3cm

C 1. 10cm   5. 14cm
    2. 4cm   6. 3.5cm
    3. 2.5cm   7. 6.5cm
    4. 11cm   8. 8.5cm

Pages 46-47

A 1. 16m   4. 24m
    2. 28m   5. 18m
    3. 22m   6. 32m

B 1. l 3cm, h 1.5cm, p 9cm
   2. l 4cm, h 1cm, p 10cm
   3. l 1.5cm, h 1.5cm, p 6cm
   4. l 2.5cm, h 3cm, p 11cm
   5. l 4cm, h 1.5cm, p 11cm
   6. l 2.5cm, h 1cm, p 7cm

Pages 46-47 Continued

C

Rectangle	length	add	height	Multiply total by 2	Perim
1	6m	+	2m	= 8m → x 2	
2	8m	+	4m	= 12m → x 2	
3	5m	+	5m	= 10m → x 2	
4	7m	+	9m	= 16m → x 2	
5	11m	+	1m	= 12m → x 2	

Pages 48-49

A 1. 9 square centimetres
   2. 5 square centimetres
   3. 7 square centimetres
   4. 6 square centimetres
   5. 10 square centimetres
   6. 6 square centimetres

B 1. 8 square metres
   2. 49 square metres
   3. 16 square metres
   4. 23 square metres
   5. 25 square metres

Pages 50-51

Challenge: Three 3-litre jugs and two
           4-litre jugs.

A 1. 80ml   4. 50ml
    2. 600ml   5. 200ml
    3. 3 litres   6. 1.5 litres

B 1. 4   2. 2   3. 1   4. 2   5. 1

C 1. 2   4. 20
    2. 10   5. 4
    3. 4   6. 5

Pages 52-53

A 1. 1kg   4. 3kg
    2. 1kg   5. 500g
    3. 250g   6. $1\frac{1}{2}$ kg (or 1500g)

B 1. 2kg   4. 6000g
    2. 5000g   5. 9000g
    3. 4kg   6. 3kg

C 1. 4kg   4. 7kg
    2. $5\frac{1}{2}$ kg   5. $8\frac{1}{2}$ kg
    3. 9 kg   6. $2\frac{1}{2}$ kg

Challenge: 4kg

Pages 54-55

Answers may be given as digital (12.10)
or in the 'o'clock' format.

A 1. 2.10   5. 7.30
    2. 4.50   6. 10.15
    3. 1.20   7. 3.45
    4. 6.05   8. 8.35

B 1. 6.45
    2. 8 o'clock
    3. 20 minutes
    4. 4.25
    5. 45 minutes

C 1. 9.05   4. 9.50
    2. 9.15   5. 9.55
    3. 9.30   6. 10.10

Pages 56-57

A 1. 3 minutes past 7
    2. 11 minutes past 3
    3. 3 minutes to 2
    4. 20 minutes to 3
    5. 22 minutes past 9
    6. 25 minutes past 4
    7. 10 minutes to 1
    8. 5 minutes to 6

B 8:36, 8:48, 9:00
    1. Sports centre 36 minutes
       Supermarket 48 minutes
    2. 36 minutes

C 1. 8 o'clock
    2. 10 minutes to 12
    3. 20 minutes to 2
    4. 20 minutes past 3
    5. 5 minutes past 9
    6. 25 minutes past 10

Pages 58-59

A 1. human   2. blue whale
    3. hummingbird   4. 35 years
    5. cat   6. 10 years
    7. leatherback turtle
    8. elephant, human and
       blue whale

B 1. 10 2. apple 3. orange 4. 7
    5. 17 6. 2 7. peach and pineapple
    8. apple and banana 9. 6

Pages 60-61

A

Name	Tally	Total
Jack	卌 III	8
Claire	卌 卌 卌 卌 卌 卌 II	32
Freddy	卌 卌 卌 I	16
Anya	卌 III	8

1. TRUE
2. FALSE
3. TRUE
4. FALSE
5. TRUE

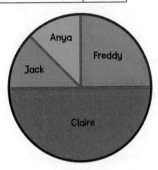

B 1. 8cm
    2. 5cm
    3. it speeds up
    4. yes

C 1. 1 person
    2. 2 people
    3. 8 people
    4. 1 person
    5. 12 people (8 + 1 + 2 + 1 = 12)

Pages 62-63

A 1. (5, 2) 2. (3, 4) 3. (2, 1)

B A (1, 1) B (1, 3) C (2, 4) D (3, 1)
    E (3, 3) F (4, 4) G (5, 2) H (6, 1)

C 1. (-3, 3) 2. (3, 3) 3. (-3, -3)
    4. (3, -3)

Answers

Page 64

A <u>spark</u>, <u>spark</u>le, <u>spark</u>ler

<u>clear</u>, <u>clear</u>ed, <u>clear</u>ly

<u>bed</u>room, <u>bed</u>stead, <u>bed</u>time

<u>sign</u>, <u>sign</u>al, <u>sign</u>ature

Page 65

B 1. eight 2. hear 3. right 4. Would 5. Where
6. beach

Page 66

A sausages, cakes, drinks, books, horses, trees

dishes, kisses, foxes, lunches, buses, wishes, crosses

ponies, babies, stories, daisies, cherries, berries

Page 67

B buds, millions, flowers, sandcastles, leaves, trees, snowmen

C 1. There are <u>mice</u> in the house! 2. There were only two
<u>loaves</u>. 3. We saw <u>geese</u> in the park.

Page 68

A untie, unlock, unlike, unlikely, unable, unfair, undo, unlucky,
unhappy, unhurt

I'm very <u>unhappy</u> with you. / It's so <u>unfair</u>! / I'm just <u>unlucky</u>!

Page 69

B Tom and Jez went to see a <u>remake</u> of *Monsters of the
Deep*. Writing about it in a movie <u>review</u> for their school
magazine, they said, "The monsters were <u>unrealistic</u> and
<u>unimaginative</u> really. There was lots of action but the plot
was <u>disjointed</u> and <u>impossible</u> to follow."

C 1. thoughtful 2. useless 3. hopeful 4. careful

Page 70

A 1. We'll have two cornets with raspberry sauce, a vanilla ice
cream, a carton of orange juice and a cup of tea, please.

2. I'd like to order the tomato soup, an egg and cress
sandwich, a banana smoothie and a chocolate muffin, please.

3. The cat ran up the stairs, down the corridor, through the
classroom and into Mrs Lane's office!

4. Go right at the lights, turn right again at the T-junction,
then first left.

5. The children bought a ball, a notebook, a pencil case and
some balloons.

Page 71

B 1. Suddenly, all the lights went out!

2. "Aaaaaaaargh!" he cried.

3. Gina called out, "Hey, Tom!"

4. "What are 'gators?" she asked.

5. How do we know there's no life on Mars?

Page 72

A 1. Tara cried, "Wait for me!"

2. "Do you think he's an elf?" asked Taylor.

3. "Okay," said Sharon. "What's wrong?"

4. "Wow!" said Zac. "You're a genius!"

B Ali and Bansi were in the Spooky Maize Maze.

"I think we must be lost," said Bansi, "because I
remember this path."

A ghostly cry came from behind the hedge: "Wooooh,
wooooooh!"

"Stop scaring me," said Ali.

"It's not me!" replied Bansi.

"Help!" they both cried.

Page 73

C The chef said, "These cakes are delicious."

D "Dogs need a healthy diet," said the vet.

E 1. Lauren said, "I feel ill."

2. Sam said, "It isn't fair."

Page 74

A 1. can't 2. shouldn't 3. they'll 4. she's 5. couldn't
6. we'll 7. where's 8. they're

B 1. Ben's shoes 2. My friend's book 3. The dog's lead
4. Joe's car 5. The cat's whiskers

Page 75

C 1. The girl's cat 2. The teacher's book
3. The family's television 4. The clown's red nose
5. The baby's pram 6. The dolls' house
7. The children's drawings
8. The men's race

Page 76

A 1. The <u>flowers</u> were pretty.

2. I live in <u>London</u>.

3. The <u>food</u> was delicious.

4. <u>Zak</u> was asleep.

5. The <u>girls</u> laughed.

6. My <u>sister</u> has a <u>laptop</u>.

Page 76 continued

B 1. The flowers were pretty so I put <u>them</u> in a vase.

2. Zak was asleep and I didn't want to wake <u>him</u> up.

3. I like London because <u>it</u> has an interesting history.

4. The girls laughed because <u>they</u> thought it was funny.

5. Chris and I went swimming. <u>We</u> had a great time.

Page 77

C Possible answers:

<u>First</u>, we had a spelling test. <u>Then</u> we wrote animal poems. <u>Before</u> lunch, we had a visitor. It was Mrs White. She'd brought her new baby to show us. <u>After</u> lunch, we had games outside on the field. <u>However</u>, <u>suddenly</u> it started to rain and we had to run inside. <u>Next</u>, it was our science lesson. <u>Finally</u>, just before home time we had a story.

Page 78

A Colours: blue, lemon, scarlet, violet, indigo.

Sizes: huge, enormous, minuscule, average, narrow.

Moods: sullen, raucous, excitable, angry, bored.

B Possible answers:

1. We had a <u>great</u> time.

2. The pizza was <u>average</u>.

3. The giant stomped his <u>huge</u> foot.

4. It was an <u>hilarious</u> movie.

Page 79

C

black 〉 white	scorching 〉 freezing
bold 〉 shy	expensive 〉 cheap
hazy 〉 clear	popular 〉 unpopular
hairy 〉 bald (or hairless)	delicious 〉 horrible (or disgusting)
unusual 〉 common (or normal)	polite 〉 rude

D Possible answers:

1. A <u>fierce</u>, <u>big</u> dog came bounding up to her.

2. It was a <u>new</u> table.

3. It was an <u>easy</u> job.

4. He was in a <u>sad</u> mood.

5. She went <u>white</u> when she saw him.

Page 80

1. <u>In the end</u>, they were happy.

2. <u>Carefully</u>, she crossed the stream.

3. <u>Back at the house</u>, there was no one home.

4. <u>When the bell rang</u>, they ran outside to play.

Page 81

B 1. In the morning, it was sunny.

2. As it turned out, they were lucky.

3. When the audience cheered, they took a bow.

4. Later that day, the storm broke.

C 1. On Saturday, the weekend begins.

2. In the middle of the wood, there was a tree house.

3. The following year, she went to Australia.

D 1. Suddenly, it went dark.

2. After school, she went to a friend's house.

3. Before Marek joined them, the team lost every match

4. When the candles were lit, they sang 'Happy Birthday'.

Page 82

A 1. It will rain on Wednesday. 2. It was sunny on Saturday.

3. It is snowing today.

B

Past	Present	Future
It was hot.	It is hot.	<u>It will be hot.</u>
I was hot.	<u>I am hot.</u>	<u>I will be hot.</u>
<u>He was hot.</u>	He is hot.	He will be hot.
We were hot.	We are hot.	<u>We will be hot.</u>
<u>They were hot.</u>	<u>They are hot.</u>	They will be hot.

Page 83

C

I am painting.	I painted.	I have painted.
I am jumping.	I jumped.	I have jumped.
I am shopping.	I shopped.	I have shopped.
I am skipping.	I skipped.	I have skipped.

D I <u>got</u> out of the car and <u>stepped</u> in a puddle. We <u>heard</u> the band playing. They <u>had</u> started already! I <u>ran</u> all the way to the hall.

Page 84

A The sentence that does not belong: The hammerhead shark has eyes on the sides of its head!

Page 85

D "I would like to be able to change the weather," said Raj, "then we could have snowball fights in summer."

"I would like x-ray vision," said Katja, "then I could find all the things I've lost in my bedroom."

Page 86

A 1. <u>When I am older</u>, I want to be an astronaut.

2. I must have grown, <u>because these trousers are too short</u>.

3. I'll meet you, <u>after I've had lunch</u>.

4. I said I was sorry, <u>although it was an accident</u>.

Answers

Page 86 continued

B When I was six, <u>I had a party</u>.
<u>I clean my teeth</u> before I go to bed.
Unless it's raining, <u>we're having a picnic</u>.
While the cat's away, <u>the mice will play!</u>

Page 87

C <u>Unless you have a better idea</u>, let's go to the cinema.
I would buy them, <u>if you like them</u>.
Stop, <u>before going any further!</u>
You can play in the garden, <u>while I cook dinner</u>.

D Run home ⟶ before it's too late!
Put the jelly in the fridge ⟶ until it sets.
I know it's time to get up ⟶ because my alarm clock is ringing.
You can go first ⟶ as it's your birthday.

Page 88

A Nouns: 1st armadillo, 2nd lemur, 3rd ostrich, 4th tarantula
Verbs: 1st knit, 2nd print, 3rd sew, 4th write

B dart ⟶ move quickly
lurch ⟶ lean to one side
quake ⟶ shake with fright
squirm ⟶ move uncomfortably
twirl ⟶ move in circles

Page 89

D 1. absent, afraid, agree, angle, apple, asleep, attach
2. quack, quarter, quell, quest, quick, quiet, quiz

Page 90

A 1. How Volcanoes Work – NF
2. Primary Science – NF
3. Bedtime Stories – F
4. Teddy Goes to Toytown – F
5. A History of the Vikings – NF
6. Treasure Island – F

Challenge: Morris and the Aliens is fiction.

Page 91

B A. Wizardy Woo B. Secrets and Spies
C. Disappearing Worlds

C Fiction: Wizardy Woo, Secrets and Spies
Non-fiction: Disappearing Worlds

Page 93

A 1. It is about the first day of the sales.
2. The customers are waiting outside.
3. She is nervous about the opening.
4. They are 'like sharks around a carcass'.
5. She is 'like an underwater swimmer moving against the current', and 'like a seashell carried on a wave'.
6. There will be mayhem as the customers fight for bargains.

Page 94

A Possible answers:
A dog was hurrying home with a big bone <u>that</u> the butcher had given him. He growled at everyone <u>who/he</u> passed, worried that they might try to steal it <u>from</u> him. He planned to bury the bone in the <u>garden</u> and eat it later.
As he crossed a bridge <u>over</u> a stream, the dog happened to look down into <u>the</u> water. There he saw another dog with a much <u>bigger</u> bone. He didn't realise he was looking at his <u>own</u> reflection! He growled at the other dog and it <u>growled</u> back.
The greedy dog wanted that bone too, and <u>he</u> snapped at the dog in the water. But then <u>his</u> own big bone fell into the stream with a <u>splash</u>, and quickly sank out of sight. Then he realised <u>how</u> foolish he had been.

Page 95

B 1. He was hurrying to get home quickly before someone stole the bone from him.
2. The other dog growled back because it was just a reflection.
3. The dog learned that he had lost his bone because he was greedy.
4. b) It is foolish to be greedy.

Page 97

B REUSE AND RECYCLE   DANCING DOGS IN SCHOOL DRAMA
TWINS ARE A TERRIBLE TWOSOME   LOOK AFTER YOUR LONG LOCKS

Pages 98-99

A 1. The extract tells us about the rats.
2. killed/cats/cradles; bit/babies
3. vats, sprats, hats, chats, flats
4. A ladle is a big spoon.
5. The apostrophe tells us that there is only one cook.
6. They all begin with an 's' sound. They also rhyme.
7. They are worn on Sunday when going to church.
8. 'With shrieking and squeaking
In fifty different sharps and flats.'

Page 100

A 1. bald, all

2. 'Thinner' rhymes with 'dinner'. When we eat we usually grow fatter so growing thinner is a sign that the Vulture isn't well.

3. The poem teaches us not to eat between meals.

4. It is not a serious poem but a fun or nonsense poem. The Vulture doesn't have a bald head and thin neck for the reasons given in the poem.

Page 101

B 1. 'Quickenham' and 'sickenham' are both made-up words, invented to rhyme with 'Twickenham'.

2. She wore the boots for a time before she took them off.

Page 103

A "A new puppy!" Buster wailed. "After everything I've done for them."

"I knew you'd be upset," replied Sindy. "I told Mindy when I heard."

"I take them for lovely walks, I eat up all their leftovers - even that takeaway muck they always dish out on a Friday... and this is the thanks I get!" said Buster.

"You can choose your friends but you can't choose your owners," said Sindy, sympathetically.

"What can they want a puppy for anyway?" cried Buster.

"Well, puppies are cute," said Sindy.

"Cute! Aren't I cute enough for them?" replied Buster.

"Er ..." said Sindy.

"Well, I'm telling you now," said Buster. "It's not getting its paws on my toys. I've buried them all!"

Page 104

A 1. She needs to leave at 2.45 pm in order to get to the appointment on time.

2. Becky's appointment is on Tuesday.

3. Mrs Kenwood apologises because Becky will miss a lesson.

4. Becky will have to do her homework because Mrs Kenwood is going to collect it.

Page 105

B 1. The kitchen company's address is on the left.

2. Shoddy means careless and of poor quality.

3. Mrs Kenwood wants the company to put right these mistakes.

4. She is exasperated, disappointed and annoyed.

Page 106

A 1. You need a plastic bag, rolling pin and glass.

2. No there isn't enough for two glasses because the ingredients list states 'serves 1'.

3. No, because the apple slices are for decoration only.

4. These words are verbs.

Page 109

A 1. Philip was angry because she was a Catholic and he was too.

2. 'It was the final straw' means that Philip will take some action.

3. The English ships could then be attacked on three sides.

4. The plan was to sail burning ships into them.

5. The English ships were smaller, faster and had better cannons.

6. The Armada was shipwrecked off the coasts of Ireland and Scotland.

7. About 65 Spanish ships survived.

8. They all survived.

Page 112

A 1. A girl, about 9 years old, who loves girlie things.

2. Princess, pretty, pink, pillows and purple; sequins, sparkled

3. She was disappointed the ring wasn't pink or purple.

4. The ring is important because we are told that it would change her world forever.

Page 114

A 1. Grandpa Bob is more likely to read books.

2. Auntie Deera is most likely to enjoy food because we are told she is plump.

3. (possible answer) Auntie Deera was tall and thin with a sharp, sullen face.

4. Zak is the youngest because the text implies that he is ten years old.

5. Charlie is probably a teenager.

Page 118

A 7, 3, 1, 5, 2, 4, 6

Answers

Page 124

A canine - tearing; molar - grinding; incisor - cutting

Page 125

B Plaque is a sticky **coating** that covers the teeth. **Microbes** live in it and make **acid** that rots your **teeth**. When you **clean** your teeth you remove the acid and **plaque** and keep your teeth **healthy**.

Page 126

A chicken leg - protein

chips and peas - fruit and vegetables

butter - fats and sugars

apple - fruit and vegetables

bread - carbohydrates

Page 127

B fish - helps you grow

bread - gives you energy

orange - keeps you healthy

Page 129

A 1.

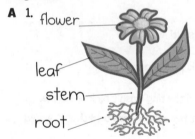

Page 130

A 1. A. The plant without leaves was shorter.

2. A. The plant grown in sunlight was green.

3. The plant has grown to try to find light.

Page 131

B 1. Too much or too little water can kill plants and there is a certain amount of water with which plants grow best (which is around 15cm³ per day for cress seedlings).

2. Warmth makes plants grow faster.

Page 132

A Basalt - F, Granite - B, Sandstone - A, Limestone - D, Chalk - E, Slate - G, Marble - C

Page 133

B 1. Granite - non-porous, limestone - porous, sandstone - porous, basalt - non-porous

2. Slate is non-porous because it keeps the rain from coming through the roof.

Page 134

A 1. Sand

2. Clay

3. B. a sieve with holes large enough for one type of particle

Page 135

B 1. A 40cm³, B 57cm³, C 29cm³

2. C   3. B

Page 136

A 1. They repel each other.

2. They attract each other.

3. They repel each other.

4. Attract

5. Repel

Page 137

B 1. C

2. A

Page 138

A 1. A will squash, B will not change.

2. A will stretch a lot, B will stretch a little.

Page 139

B 1. about 5cm

2. about 30cm

Page 140

A Torch A

Page 141

B Clear plastic TP, window glass TP, wood O, water TP, frosted glass TL, brick O, cardboard O, metal O, greaseproof paper TL, orange juice O

Page 142

A A 13.00 B 09.00 C 14.30

Page 143

B A - false, B - true, C - true

Page 144

A thigh bone - pelvis, arm bone - collar bone, rib cage - spine

Page 145

B   slug - water skeleton
frog and snake - skeleton of bone
shrimp and spider - skeleton of armour

Page 147

A The heart

The heart is a muscle that **pumps** blood around the body. Blood takes **food** and oxygen to all parts of the body. When the muscles exercise, they need more food and **oxygen** so the heart pumps faster.

Exercise and fat

Energy from food is **stored** in the body as fat. Too much **fat** makes the body heavy and puts a strain on muscles and the heart. Exercise uses up **energy** and stops the body getting overweight.

Page 148

A   A is a habitat, B is a mini habitat, C and D are micro habitats.

Page 149

B The forest habitat

Trees make the forest **shady**. Plants such as **ferns** and **mosses** can grow here. They are adapted to growing in dim light.

The pond habitat

A freshwater pond is cool and **wet**. Organisms such as **fish** and **waterlilies** can survive here. They are adapted to living in fresh water.

The rocky shore habitat

A rocky shore is partly covered by **salt** water. Organisms such as **limpets** and **crabs** can survive here. They are adapted to the salty waves.

Page 150

A   1. insects - D, spiders - A, fish - G,
amphibians - E, reptiles - B, birds - F,
mammals - C
2. Humans belong to the mammal group.

Page 151

B   A - horse chestnut, B - beech, C - ash,
D - holly, E - oak, F - lime

Page 152

A   1. lettuce (or any other plant food) > human
2. grain (or grass) > chicken (or sheep, cattle) > human

Page 154

Page 155

B   1.

Time from start (minutes)	Temperature (°C)
0	35
1	30
2	25
3	20
4	20

2. The water had cooled to room temperature.

3.

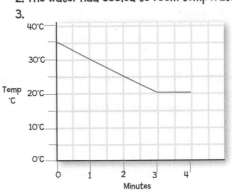

Answers

Page 156

A 1. The cup without the material makes the test fair by showing how each material affects cooling.
2. wool
3. aluminium foil

Page 157

B 1. C - the steel spoon
2. The butter would melt because aluminium is a metal like steel and metals are good conductors.
3. The heat passes quickly from the pan to the food and speeds up cooking.
Challenge: Pan handles are made of insulating materials like wood or plastic so hands are not burned.

Page 158

A 1. A - 10cm³, B - 30cm³
2. 40cm³

Page 159

B 1. The same volume of liquid is used and the slope is kept at the same angle.
A - 8 seconds, B - 20 seconds, C - 6 seconds

Page 160

A 1. A, C, B, D
2. B and D
3. 650°C

Page 161

B The molten rock **flowing** down the **side** of a volcano is a **liquid** and may be as **hot** as 1200°C. It cools as it moves **away** and when it reaches **600 °C** it stops flowing and becomes **solid** rock. The **freezing** point of the rock is 600°C.

Page 162

A 1. Sugar, instant coffee granules, salt
2. Some substances in the tea leaves dissolve in the water but the leaf does not.

Page 163

B 1. a
2. c.
3. Yes. The holes let the dissolved substance pass through but keep the leaves in the bag.

Page 164

A A - 3N, B - 5N, C - 8N, D - 4N

Page 165

B 1. sandpaper
2. velvet
3. newspaper
4. plastic sheet

Page 166

A Sound travels fastest through solids. Sound travels slowest through gases.

Page 167

B 1. By wrapping the same thickness of each material tested around the sound source.
2. B was the best insulator.

Page 168

A motor - provides movement
wire - conducts electricity
buzzer - makes a sound
switch - controls the flow of electricity

Page 169

B No. There is a gap in the circuit next to the battery's positive terminal.

Page 170

A 1. steel spoon - conductor, wooden spoon - insulator, copper pipe - conductor, plastic comb - insulator
2. Air is an insulator. If it was a conductor the lamp would light when there was no other material in the gap.

Page 171

B When the tube is **tipped**, the **ball bearing** rolls onto the ends of the **wires** and **electricity** can flow through it from one wire to the next.

Page 172

A A and D allow electricity to flow.

Page 173

B B will shine more dimly.

Notes

Notes

Notes

Index

Index